CONVERSATIONS
ON
Chelation
AND MINERAL
NUTRITION

Keats Titles of Related Interest

The Nutrition Desk Reference	Robert H. Garrison, R.Ph., Ph.D. and Elizabeth Somer, M.A., R.D.
Minerals and Your Health	Len Mervyn, Ph.D.
Selenium as Food and Medicine	Richard A. Passwater, Ph.D.
Mental and Elemental Nutrients	Carl C. Pfeiffer, M.D., Ph.D.
Zinc and Other Micro-Nutrients	Carl C. Pfeiffer, M.D., Ph.D.
Nutritional Influences on Illness	Melvyn R. Werbach, M.D.
The Calcium Plus Workbook	Evelyn P. Whitlock, M.D.

CONVERSATIONS
ON
Chelation
AND MINERAL
NUTRITION

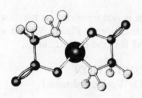

H. DEWAYNE ASHMEAD

Ph.D., Fellow of the American College of Nutrition

Foreword by Professor Boyd Beck
Snow College

KEATS PUBLISHING, INC.
New Canaan, Connecticut

Conversations on Chelation is not intended as medical advice. Its intent is solely informational and educational. Please consult a medical or health professional should the need for one be indicated.

Library of Congress Cataloging-in-Publication Data

Ashmead, H. DeWayne.
    Conversations on chelation and mineral nutrition.

    Includes index.
    1. Minerals in human nutrition. 2. Chelates--
Physiological effect. 3. Malnutrition. I. Title.
QP533.A84 1989   612.3'92   89-15371
ISBN 0-87983-501-X

Printed in the United States of America

Published by Keats Publishing, Inc.
27 Pine Street (Box 876)
New Canaan, Connecticut 06840

This book is dedicated to all those whose research made the information contained in this volume possible

Contents

vii

Foreword

Considerable progress has been made over the past three decades in the understanding of mineral nutrition, especially as it relates to chelation. The author uses conversations in which you are allowed to "listen in" to convey this understanding to you, the reader. This technique is effectively used to provide insight into such topics as the physiology of mineral nutrition in man and animals, the role of chelation in absorption and metabolism of metals, and the concept of undernutrition as it relates to clinical observations of mineral deficiencies. Separate chapters are devoted to each mineral for easy reference and clearer perception of the beneficial and detrimental effects of each mineral.

Our bodies are often compared to a chemical factory, but if the supplies for a chemical factory were always chosen by what was readily available at the time or what looked good, I would be very concerned about the types of products this factory would produce. Like chemical factories, our bodies need certain critical supplies called vitamins and minerals in order to carry out life functions effectively. These materials allow enzymes to catalyze chemical reactions, which are the chemistry of life. This book makes clear the important part these materials play in disease prevention and in providing quality of life.

I have followed with interest the progress that has been made in the area of metal chelation chemistry over the past twelve years. I did experiments in the mid-1970s that convinced me that metal chelates are absorbed much more readily than inorganic salts. In the early 1980s I helped with the development of anion-free chelates. More recently I have been excited to learn of the development of special amino acid chelates that provide targeting to specific areas of the body. This book has given me a broader picture of metal chelation as it applies to mineral nutrition.

Although mineral nutrition is a complex subject, I was impressed with the author's ability to describe the use of the scientific method to answer critical questions. Isotope data, absorption studies, and clinical observations were all used to demonstrate the important role of metal chelates in absorption and metabolism of metals. This book not only provides insight into what scientific research has discovered in this area, but also gives an appreciation of what is yet to be learned in the area of chelation and mineral nutrition.

Boyd Beck, Ph.D.
Chairman, Natural Science Division
Snow College

CONVERSATIONS
ON
Chelation
AND MINERAL
NUTRITION

1

Malnutrition versus Undernutrition

S hortly after World War II, the newly organized United Nations established the Food and Agricultural Organization (FAO) for the purpose of devising ways to improve the nutritional status of the world's population. Such a goal, it was felt, would provide a major pathway to lasting peace by helping to alleviate the alarming problem of malnutrition and starvation so prevalent in the developing countries. At the time the FAO was organized, it was estimated that there were 500 to 600 million persons throughout the world who were either starving or malnourished. According to the United Nations, lasting peace was impossible under such devastating conditions because starving people become irritable and frequently commit aggressive acts to alleviate their suffering.

Over four decades later, the number of malnourished or starving people throughout the world has risen to approximately one billion, with little hope for any relief in this plague of hunger and misery. Although the FAO has been successful in identifying specific needs and focusing public awareness on the gravity of the world hunger situation, the organization has been unable to solve the nutritional problems of the world.

The International Food Research Institute has projected that developing countries will fall 1.45 million metric tons short of demand for food by the year 1990. Amidst this great disparity between food supplies and those in desperate need, the world greets approximately ten million newborn babies each month.

It has been shown that malnutrition causes millions of premature deaths each year. These deaths range from schistosomiasis in Africa to heart disease or cancer in the United States. In some developing countries, 40 percent of the children die before reaching the age of five years. A large portion of the surviving 60 percent suffer learning disabilities, reduced working capacities, and recurring illness attributable in a great measure to their inadequate diets.

At one time I had the pleasure of visiting with a doctor who was the Swiss representative to the United Nations and one of the principal advisers to the FAO. During our conversation, we discussed some of the alarming statistics cited earlier on the extent of malnutrition and starvation around the world.

"You're fortunate you live in such an affluent society," he summarized. "In the underdeveloped countries, more than half of all deaths occur among children; whereas in countries like yours, the figure is only 5 percent."

I nodded in agreement as I conjured up visions of my own children running carefree through the grass at play. I visualized them working diligently in their schools, gaining immeasurable benefits from their educational opportunities. I reflected that the only factor limiting their growth and development was their own ambition. I couldn't begin to count the number of times they had pushed away from the dinner table, leaving partially eaten portions of food on their plates because they had been given too much to eat. Yes, my visitor was right. I was fortunate to live in this country.

"You probably have a legitimate reason for saying that we in the United States are fortunate," I told him, "but even here nutrition falls short of what it could be. As a consequence, our children suffer similarly to those in underdeveloped countries.

"For example, a few years ago a woman both my wife and I know very well became pregnant with her first child. Both she and her husband were college educated and had a reasonable income. Nevertheless, for one reason or another she did not eat properly during her pregnancy. When her baby was born, he was physically small and very susceptible to the numerous diseases of infancy. As I watched him grow and develop, I noticed that even though genetically he should have had reasonably high intelligence, he was only average or perhaps even somewhat below average.

"Now contrast this child with his younger brother who was born two years later. In her second pregnancy this woman changed and improved her diet over what it had been during her first pregnancy. When the second child was born, he was larger, noticeably stronger and much more resistant to disease than his brother had been. Mentally he grew at a much faster rate than his brother had done, and by age four he matched his six-year-old brother physically and was using approximately the same vocabulary. Based on my observations of that family, it appears that the only major reason for the differences between the two children was the nutrition of their mother during pregnancy."

"Yes, but that's an isolated incident," argued my visitor. "The real problem is infant malnutrition in underdeveloped countries around the world."

"While I don't disagree with your observations about underdeveloped countries," I countered, "I believe we often overlook the same problem in more affluent countries because the problems are not quite so acute or apparent. But, as you have pointed out, learning is at an optimum when the child is in good health and properly nourished. When children are sick or malnourished, their limited energy must be channeled solely to maintenance of bodily functions. In these situations a small amount of learning takes place. The motivation of the children drops and they lose interest in setting goals or pursuing academic tasks. Remember, nutrition starts during pregnancy."

"Yes, I agree," he said, "but we in the United Nations organization see so much more of this in underdeveloped countries."

"Do you really?" I challenged.

"What do you mean?" he wanted to know.

"Let's limit our discussion to just one aspect of malnutrition, that of intellectual development," I said. "I've been reading the studies of Doctors John Dobbing and Jean Sands of the University of Manchester in England, who suggest that an infant deprived of proper nutrition will never develop to his or her full mental capacity. Once the damage is done there is no second chance."

"What do you mean?" my friend asked.

"Like you, I have traveled in underdeveloped countries. I have seen the bloated stomachs, the stick-thin arms and legs, and the sad, listless eyes that indicate severe malnutrition. These images have been burned into my conscience, and I often feel guilty at my own abundance. But less dramatic, and therefore all the more insidious, are the long-term effects of undernutrition."

"Undernutrition?" the doctor asked.

"Yes, undernutrition." I answered. "Although these children are not starving to death, as are those you have pictured in the underdeveloped countries, their diets are imbalanced. They may lack adequate protein, vitamins, or minerals. The intake of carbohydrates may be excessive or there may be any number of other nutritional problems. One of the major consequences of undernutrition may be in the area of early brain development.

"During the early stages of brain development an adequate supply of nutrients is required at all times. Dr. Dobbing's research disclosed that, without the necessary flow of nutrients, the brain is unable to create the complex structure of cellwiring and circuits that fuse together to form a functioning human mind. During this critical period, the brain's genetic potential must be reached or forever function below its possible genetic capacity. If the infant is deprived of the correct balance of nutrients during the development of the brain, optimum mental capacity will never be reached. Today over 300 million children suffer from 'starved brains,' and it is estimated that 70 percent of the world's population is currently suffering from the effects of prenatal underdevelopment of the brain!

"In a symposium on malnutrition during pregnancy and early neonatal life sponsored by the March of Dimes, Dr. Ruth

Widdowson, an outstanding researcher from Great Britain, came to New York especially to make the March of Dimes presentation. Dr. Widdowson is an active researcher doing clinical work at hospitals as well as in the laboratory environment. In her remarks she related that fetal undernutrition is due to inadequate or unavailable nutrients which curtail both placental and fetal growth by retarding the rate of cellular division and reducing the physical size of the body cells. Her research showed that offspring developed within this type of intrauterine environment will carry these cellular defects the rest of their lives."

"I am beginning to see that undernutrition is every bit as serious as malnutrition," my guest conceded, "but how do you justify your position that the majority of the people in the United States are suffering from undernutrition?"

Walking over to my bookcase and extracting a publication by the United States government entitled *Human Nutrition, An Evaluation of Research in the United States,* I handed it to my visitor. As he opened it to the first underlined page he read, "Most all of the health problems underlying the leading causes of death in the United States could be modified by improvements in the diet. Death rates for many of these conditions are higher in the United States than in other countries of comparable economic development."

As he returned the book to me, I said, "Let's not even consider the reductions in heart disease, cancer, or respiratory infections that could result from changes in our diets. Let's just consider the twenty-five million people that have mental health disabilities. Overall, mental health problems in this country could be reduced by 10 percent with some simple improvements in diet. Infant mortality could be cut in half, with 20 percent fewer birth defects in those infants that survive. Further, job productivity, as measured by the number of employee sick days taken annually, could be increased by 5 percent. Deaths among those already undergoing medical attention could be reduced by nearly 25 percent simply by improving the diets of people in the United States. It is estimated that 12 percent of the school-age children now need special education. We could raise their IQ's 10 points simply by improving their diets.

The doctor challenged that statistic, so I told him about the study published in the January 1988 issue of *Lancet* by Doctors Benton and Roberts. Using 60 twelve- and thirteen-year-old children, who were divided into two groups, they gave one group a multivitamin and mineral supplement and the other half a placebo, which looked exactly like the supplement but had no nutritional value. After eight months the group that received the vitamins and minerals showed a significant increase in nonverbal intelligence whereas the other group did not increase their IQ's at all.

Returning to the government publication I had shown my visitor earlier, I read, "Most nutritionists and clinicians feel that the real potential from improved diet is preventative in that it may defer or modify the development of a disease state so that a clinical condition does not develop." That brought to mind a situation I had seen on a farm a few years earlier, so I told my visitor about it in order to illustrate my point.

"A farmer I knew bought about twenty baby calves from out of state," I related. "Shortly after they arrived at his farm they began to develop respiratory problems. Several of the young animals contracted pneumonia and died. The postmortem confirmed that pneumonia was the cause of their deaths, but also noted that the calves were suffering from severe malnutrition. The veterinarian who conducted the autopsies concluded that, had the animals been more nutritionally fit, they could have probably withstood the stress of being shipped to the new farm and not have contracted the respiratory infections that eventually killed them."

After relating that incident I added that in my opinion the same thing applied to human beings. When our nutrition is not adequate, we are probably more susceptible to diseases that have the potential to kill us. It isn't the malnutrition per se that kills; however, the malnutrition creates conditions within our bodies that leave us more vulnerable to the diseases.

"You have made your point," my guest said. "I'm beginning

to believe that the whole world is suffering from either malnutrition or undernutrition. Tell me, what do you believe is the major cause of our nutritional problems?"

"Lack of minerals in the diet is a major factor," I answered unhesitantly. "In the study by Benton and Roberts, which I mentioned earlier, they found that school-age children were consuming enough vitamins to approach the US Recommended Dietary Allowance, but that mineral deficiencies were common. Although by weight minerals are not a large factor in the bodies of man or animals, or even plants for that matter, they are involved in almost every physiological function necessary to sustain life. We cannot grow and develop without minerals. Our body processes cannot be regulated without minerals, and without minerals we cannot extract energy from the foods we eat."

Opening the government publication on human nutrition again, I said, "Let me read the conclusion of these government studies. 'The highest death rate areas in the country generally correspond to those where agriculturalists have recognized the soil as being depleted for several years. This suggests a possible relationship between submarginal diets and the health of succeeding generations.' "

Putting the book down I said, "Soils can be deficient in only one thing as far as plants are concerned, and that is minerals. In spite of modern fertilizing technology, the problems of mineral depletion in plants continues to worsen, particularly with trace minerals.

"For example, in a four-year study involving Albion Laboratories, 1,000 crop samples were taken from farms in eleven midwestern states. These samples were analyzed for their levels of calcium, phosphorus, potassium, sodium, magnesium, iron, copper, zinc, and manganese. The following year, 1,000 new crop samples from the same sites on the same farms were taken and analyzed. This procedure was repeated again for the next two years. When the data from the four-year study were tabulated, an unmistakable decline in the trace mineral contents was noted. In corn, calcium dropped

41 percent, phosphorus 8 percent, potassium 28 percent, sodium 55 percent, magnesium 22 percent, iron 26 percent, copper 68 percent, zinc 10 percent, and manganese 34 percent.

"As has already been pointed out in the government publications I have shown you, the US Department of Agriculture has confirmed that the depletion of these minerals in the soil and plants frequently relates to health problems in humans."

"If it is that serious in the United States, I can imagine how much greater the problem is in many other parts of the world!" the United Nations visitor exclaimed. "That certainly helps explain why iron deficiency anemia is the biggest single disease in the world today. But what are you doing about this loss of minerals in your own diet?"

"In my family I've taken several steps," I explained. "Since I have no real assurance that the food we are eating contains sufficient minerals to give us maximum benefit, we supplement our diet with minerals that have been properly chelated with amino acids. In addition, we use properly chelated minerals as part of our garden fertilizer program. Although our garden produce doesn't constitute all of the food we consume, we are at least assured that this part of our food has good nutritional content."

"How do you know your garden produce has higher nutrient content?" he asked.

"Through chemical analysis of the plants," I replied. "Not only is the mineral content up, but also the protein content. Minerals are necessary in the production of plant proteins."

"These types of nutritional programs are what is needed worldwide," my visitor declared. "There are 500 million starving people around the world, each with a right to proper nutrition and health." Then he added that perhaps with my help we may be able to correct some of these problems.

That is one of the purposes of this book. Before we can correct a problem, we must know what to do. This book points the direction to the solution to some of our problems.

ADDITIONAL READING

Guthrie, H., *Introductory Nutrition* (St. Louis: Times Mirror/ Mosby College Publishing), 1986.

Deseret News, "U.N. looks to Utah," 10 B, Tuesday, July 12, 1977.

Ashmead, H., "The starving world," paper presented at FAO meeting of United Nations, Rome, Italy, June 5, 1977.

Widdowson, R., "Malnutrition during pregnancy and early neonatal life," presented at a symposium on fetal malnutrition, New York, 1970.

Lewin, R., "Starved Brains," *Psychology Today*, 9:29, September 1975.

Feedstuffs, "Decline in Trace Minerals in Grain Shown," V. 41, 7, August 9, 1969.

Weir, C., *Benefits from Human Nutrition Research, Human Nutrition Report No. 2* (Washington, D.C.: US Department of Agriculture), 1971.

Benton, D. and Roberts, G., "Effect of vitamin and mineral supplementation on intelligence of a sample of school children," *Lancet*, 140, January 23, 1988.

Morley, J., *et al.*, eds., *Nutritional Modulation of Neural Function* (San Diego: Academic Press, Inc.), 1988.

Dobbing, J., ed., *Early Nutrition and Later Achievement* (London: Academic Press), 1987.

Seelig, M., ed., *Nutritional Imbalances in Infant and Adult Disease* (New York: Spectrum Publications, Inc.), 1977.

2

The Roles of Minerals
in the Body

W henever we think of nutritional supplements, the first
thing that usually comes to mind is vitamins. Important as vitamins are to human growth and development, we
should give a great deal more thought to the body's use of and
need for minerals.

Dr. Charles Northen has said, "The role of the trace
[minerals] is one of participation in the activities of hormones
and enzymes, a role in all probability analogous to that of
vitamins." It is not commonly realized that vitamins generally
control the body's appropriation of minerals, and in the
absence of the minerals, they frequently are unable to function. Lacking vitamins, the system can make some use of the
minerals, but lacking minerals, the vitamins are often useless.

While our bodies can manufacture some of the vitamins we
need, they must rely completely upon outside sources for an
adequate supply of minerals. These outside sources include
foods and mineral supplements. We also breathe minerals
from the air and absorb them through the skin, but these
sources yield such a minute amount of minerals that they
should not even be considered.

If we don't get enough essential minerals from food and
supplements, the total well-being of our bodies can be placed
in jeopardy. It has been estimated that minerals are involved
in more body processes than perhaps any other basic nutrient—
including protein, vitamins, fats, carbohydrates, and water.
All of these other nutrients are, without question, essential to

11

our health and well-being. But minerals play such key roles in our body's metabolism that a deficiency of any one of them seriously hampers many of our bodily processes by making these other nutrients less effective in performing their various functions within the body.

Minerals are extremely important in the makeup of a healthy body. There are ninety-two naturally occurring chemical elements on the Periodic Table, and at least fifty of them are found in the tissues and fluids of the body. Four of the elements—carbon, oxygen, hydrogen, and nitrogen—contribute about 96 percent of the total weight of the body and account for 99 percent of all the atoms in the body. The remaining 4 percent of the body weight and 1 percent of body atoms are composed of essential and nonessential minerals and mineral contaminants.

Adapting from the criteria established by G. Cotzias as early as 1967, a mineral can be classified as essential if (1) it is present in the healthy tissues of the living body, (2) its concentration in similar animals and human beings is fairly constant, (3) upon withdrawal from the body, reproducible structural and/or physiological abnormalities result, (4) the addition of the deficient mineral corrects the above-mentioned abnormalities, (5) an induced deficiency of a specific mineral is always accompanied by a pertinent specific biochemical change, and (6) the above-mentioned biochemical change can be prevented or corrected when the mineral deficiency is prevented or corrected. However, the mere presence of a mineral in the tissues of animals or human beings does not prove that it is essential. Some of these minerals—such as lead or arsenic—are detrimental to the overall health and performance of the body.

Recently, I picked up a brochure on a special mineral water, which the bottler was claiming was of exceptional benefit to the body. As I read the long list of minerals, I was astounded to see that this water contained not only lead and mercury, but also nickel, which has been incriminated as being carcinogenic, and arsenic, a deadly poison. There were other minerals that were equally detrimental in the water, so I was shocked that the company advocated taking four ounces of this "natural water" with each meal. I contacted the company to ask what the benefits of this water were. The response was, "Each body is different. You will have to try it and see what it does." I politely declined.

The essential macrominerals, that is, minerals required in dietary amounts of 100 milligrams (mg) or more per day, include calcium, phosphorus, sodium, potassium, chlorine, magnesium, and sulfur. Essential microminerals, which are minerals needed in quantities of only a few milligrams or micrograms (mcg) each day, are iron, copper, cobalt, zinc, manganese, iodine, molybdenum, selenium, fluorine, and chromium. Several microminerals that may be but have not proven to be essential for life include tin, silicon, boron, and vanadium. Nonessential contaminants include lead, cadmium, mercury, arsenic, barium, strontium, aluminum, lithium, beryllium, rubidium, as well as some others. Figure 2-1 illustrates these proportions as they relate to human beings.

Although the essential microminerals comprise only a small fraction of the total body weight, they are absolutely crucial in aiding the extraction of energy from carbohydrates, fats, and protein; in growth and maintenance of body tissue; and in assisting in the regulation of body processes. Widdowson and Dickerson have written: "Even small departures from the normal mineral composition of the milieu interieur [the interior of the cell] may have profound physiological consequences, but may make no appreciable difference to the composition of the body as a whole."[1]

The late Professor E. Underwood has added that "the characteristic concentrations and functional forms of these elements must be maintained within narrow limits if the functional and structural integrity of the tissues is to be safeguarded and the growth, health, and fertility of man are to remain unimpaired."[2]

At a nutritional convention in London some years ago, I

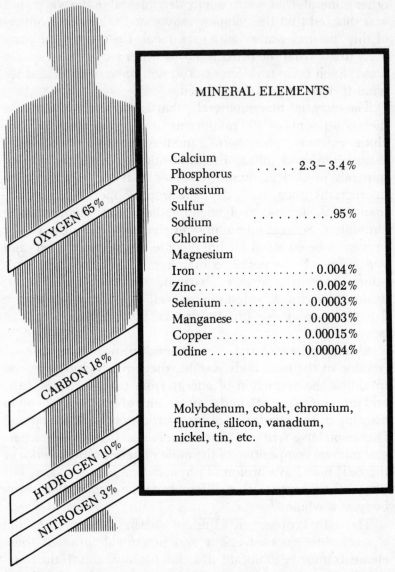

MINERAL ELEMENTS

Calcium
Phosphorus   . . . . . 2.3 – 3.4%
Potassium
Sulfur
Sodium 95%
Chlorine
Magnesium
Iron 0.004%
Zinc 0.002%
Selenium 0.0003%
Manganese 0.0003%
Copper 0.00015%
Iodine 0.00004%

Molybdenum, cobalt, chromium,
fluorine, silicon, vanadium,
nickel, tin, etc.

OXYGEN 65%

CARBON 18%

HYDROGEN 10%

NITROGEN 3%

Figure 2 – 1. **Body elemental composition.** SOURCE: Courtesy of
H.D. Ashmead *et al.*, *Intestinal Absorption of Metal Ions and Chelates* (Springfield: Charles C Thomas, 1985), p. 4.

was asked to lecture on mineral nutrition. Following my lecture, which emphasized the importance of minerals in relation to other body nutrients, a group of people came to the podium to ask some more specific questions.

"I can see the need for calcium in our bones and teeth, and iron for our blood," said a silver-haired lady, stepping to the front of the group, "but what about all of these other minerals you have talked about? Of what use are they?"

"Most minerals play more than one role in the body," I explained. "For example, you mentioned the need of calcium for bones and teeth. This is an excellent illustration of the use of a mineral for growth and maintenance of the body. If we didn't have the calcium to help form our bones, we would be as limp as a jellyfish.

"However, even the jellyfish needs calcium in its body to survive," I continued. "Like the jellyfish, the human body is made up of a multitude of cells. Each one of these cells is covered by a protective membrane known as the cell wall. Chelated calcium in the cell membrane helps govern the permeability of the cell wall. By governing permeability, the calcium controls the absorption of nutrients into the cell as well as the excretion of wastes out of the cell. In this role the calcium is carrying out a second function, that of regulating a body process."

As another listener raised a hand to ask me another question, I asked him to wait a minute and continued, "We often think of iron as functioning only in the production of hemoglobin in the blood. As part of the hemoglobin molecule, iron aids in the transportation of oxygen throughout the body to help each one of the cells breathe. Without iron, we would suffocate even while swimming in pure oxygen. Thus, within the hemoglobin molecule, chelated iron helps to regulate a body process.

"Many of us have observed that when we are anemic we are tired, so we frequently conclude that being anemic makes us tired. But anemia, or the lack of hemoglobin in the blood, has absolutely nothing to do with being tired. That does not mean that an iron deficiency is not related to being tired. However, it is a separate function of the iron, which, when disrupted, results in a lack of energy. When the body converts fat, carbohydrates, or protein into energy, these nutrients undergo several metabolic changes. One of the groups of changes is lumped into the Krebs Cycle, named for the scientist who discovered it. Chelated iron is involved in the activation of certain enzymes within this cycle. The changes necessary to convert nutrients into energy occur only when the iron is available in certain enzymes. In its absence, the metabolic pathway may be partially or totally blocked, resulting in the reduction of the energy that is needed to keep the body functioning properly. Under such conditions, the body experiences fatigue."

"You mentioned enzymes," said another woman. "Exactly what are enzymes and what is their function in the body?" "That's an important question," I answered. "As I said earlier, our bodies are made up of billions of individual cells. When we eat protein it is digested down into amino acids, which are ultimately moved through the cell membranes into the cells themselves. The cell uses amino acids in many different ways. Just as we use wood to build houses, make furniture, or make baseball bats, the cells use these amino acids for energy, for rebuilding themselves, and for regulating body processes. But before the amino acids can regulate body processes, they are usually restructured into proteinase material called enzymes. After these enzymes are produced, some of them are secreted into the body fluids while others are simply retained within the cell's structure and utilized there. Enzymes assist in converting proteins, vitamins, fats, and carbohydrates in the body from one form to another. In other words, they help to stimulate chemical reactions. The enzymes play unique parts in chemical reactions since they are not changed by the processes but merely act as catalysts and speed up the reactions.

"These enzyme reactions are vitally important in keeping us alive," I continued. "For example, it is estimated by some biochemists that some cells in the body, such as the cells which make up the heart, perform up to an estimated 2.5 million enzyme reactions in each cell each minute. Multiply those reactions by the number of cells that make up the heart muscle and you are quickly into many billions of enzyme reactions per minute.

"Many enzymes do not work by themselves, but need the help of an activator. This activator is generally a specific mineral, often coupled with a vitamin. To illustrate, cellular division, which is required for growth as well as maintenance of the adult body, requires many enzyme reactions. One specific enzyme, DNA ligase, helps to produce the genetic material for the new cell. Even if the DNA ligase enzyme is present in the cell, it won't work unless zinc is placed inside the enzyme to activate it. And even if the zinc is present in the cell, it can't get into the enzyme until the vitamin niacin picks it up and places it there."

"That sounds terribly complicated," said another listener.

"It is," I agreed. "Scientists are just now starting to understand the many roles minerals and vitamins play in activating enzymes. They are finding that in some instances an absence of a specific mineral totally blocks the enzyme activity. In other cases, if one mineral is deficient, the enzyme will select another to use in its place. It has been learned that an excess of one mineral may overstimulate a certain enzyme. Such a reaction can result in metabolic problems that are just as detrimental as the failure of the enzymatic reaction."

"From what you are saying," suggested another man who had been quietly listening to our conversation, "it appears that one of the biggest roles of minerals in the body is to activate enzymes."

"That's right," I agreed. "Certainly macrominerals such as calcium and phosphorus play major nonenzymatic roles in giving structure to our bodies through the formation of bones and teeth, but the trace elements function primarily as catalysts in enzyme systems within the cells and body fluids. In fact, it is primarily in this function, as an enzyme catalyst, that minerals are able to help our bodies grow and maintain themselves, regulate body processes, and supply us with energy. Minerals do this by inducing or maintaining the enzyme in an active state, by being an essential part of the enzyme, or by actually changing the molecular structure of the compound being converted."

Reaching into my briefcase I pulled out one volume of a series of books entitled *Mineral Metabolism*. Opening it to a page pertaining to our discussion, I said, "The authors have written that some diseases are characterized by alterations in the concentrations of specific minerals in the fluids that surround our body cells. Furthermore, when there are very slight changes from the normal mineral composition inside the cell, this alteration may result in profound physiological consequences without making any appreciable difference in the total mineral makeup of the body."

I replaced the book in my briefcase and continued, "In other words, what these researchers are saying is that we only need a minute amount of a specific mineral to work with an enzyme. Consider, again, the cells in the heart muscle. Each one is about 5/25,000 of an inch in diameter. One thousand of them could be placed on the head of a pin without any problem. Within each one of these heart cells there are more than 1,000 mitochondria—chemical factories—where iron is required for the production of energy. If we short-change those heart-muscle cells on the amount of iron they must have, the necessary enzymes that convert the absorbed nutrients into energy can't work. Should these energy-producing enzymes malfunction, the heart cells would be unable to keep the heart beating. Even though a person might die as a result of his or her heart cells being iron-deficient, it would be extremely difficult to measure any loss of body iron since the amount required for this specific enzymatic function is so minute."

"What you are saying is that no one other nutrient has any greater effect on us than the minerals," concluded another listener.

"We cannot survive without the other essential nutrients, but I believe that minerals are far more important than most people understand," I answered. "Scientists are daily discovering new enzymatic roles for the minerals we know exist in our bodies. Ultimately, I believe we will be able to show that almost everything that occurs in the body is dependent upon a specific mineral being in the right enzyme at the right time."

"I believe that this is one of the major reasons why the United States government concluded in the book *Dietary Goals for the United States* that most of the health problems which are responsible for death in the United States could be modified by improvements in the diet. That includes improvements in mineral nutrition. For example, the government concluded that kidney and urinary disease deaths could be reduced by 20 percent. In the case of cancer, 20 percent of the people who died could have been saved by changing their diets. In the case of osteoporosis, a demineralization of the bones which affects approximately 4 million Americans, the United States government reports that by improving the American diet we could reduce this disease by some 75 percent."

Apparently the statistics I had presented to the group of listeners were frightening enough to keep them from pursuing the topic any longer, and the crowd began to disperse.

NOTES

1. C. Comar and F. Bronner, eds., *Mineral Metabolism*, Vol. 2 (New York: Academic Press, 1964), p. 57.
2. E. Underwood, *Trace Elements in Human and Animal Nutrition* (New York: Academic Press, 1977), p. 7.

ADDITIONAL READING

Ashmead, H. D., *et al.*, *Intestinal Absorption of Metal Ions and Chelates* (Springfield: Charles C Thomas), 1985.
Cotzias, G. and Hemphill, D., eds., *Proceedings of First Annual Conference on Trace Substances and Environmental Health* (Columbia: University of Missouri), 5, 1967.
Ashmead, H., "Nickel and cancer," paper given at the 10th annual

convention of International Association of Cancer Victims and Friends, Los Angeles, September 1973.

Widdowson, E. and Dickerson, J., "Chemical composition of the body," in Comar, C. and Bronner, F., eds., *Mineral Metabolism* (New York: Academic Press), V. 2, 1 – 247, 1964.

Underwood, E., *Trace Elements in Human and Animal Nutrition* (New York: Academic Press), 1977.

Ashmead, H., "Tissue transportation of organic trace minerals," *J. Appl. Nutri.* 22:42, Spring 1970.

Gallagher, C., *Nutritional Factors and Enzymological Disturbances in Animals* (Philadelphia: J.B. Lippincott Co.), 1964.

Giese, A., *Cell Physiology* (Philadelphia: Saunders College), 1973.

Weir, C., *Benefits from Human Nutrition Research, Human Nutrition Report No. 2* (Washington, D.C.: US Department of Agriculture), 1971.

Wilson, E. *et al.*, *Principles of Nutrition* (New York: John Wiley & Sons), 1979.

Comar, C. and Bronner, F., eds., *Mineral Metabolism: An Advanced Treatise*, 3 volumes (New York: Academic Press), 1960, 1962, 1964 and 1969.

3

Why Are Chelated
Minerals Important?

As I travel throughout the world talking about mineral nutrition, I am frequently asked, "Why is chelation of those minerals so important to good mineral nutrition?"

Perhaps the easiest way to answer this question is to first define what a chelated mineral is. By definition a chelate is formed when two or more separate and unique portions of the same ligand molecule, which in this case is an amino acid, form coordinate covalent and ionic bonds with the same atom of metal. The binding sites on the amino acid are the alpha amino and carboxyl moieties. The resulting five-member ring structure consists of the metal atom, the active carboxyl oxygen atom, the carboxyl carbon atom, the alpha carbon atom, and the alpha nitrogen atom as seen in Figure 3-1 in which two amino acids are chelated to the metal.

At least two and sometimes three amino acids can be bound to the same metal atom, creating bicyclic and tricyclic ringed molecules. The bicyclic version can be visualized by holding a marble between the thumb and index finger of one hand and then additionally joining the thumb and index finger of the other hand to the same marble at the same time. The marble would represent the metal atom and the hands would represent the amino acid ligands, each joined to the same metal atom at different sites on the same molecule (at the carboxyl and alpha amino moieties). A second person could lend an additional hand to grasp the marble in the same manner and conceptualize the structure of a tricyclic amino acid chelate.

21

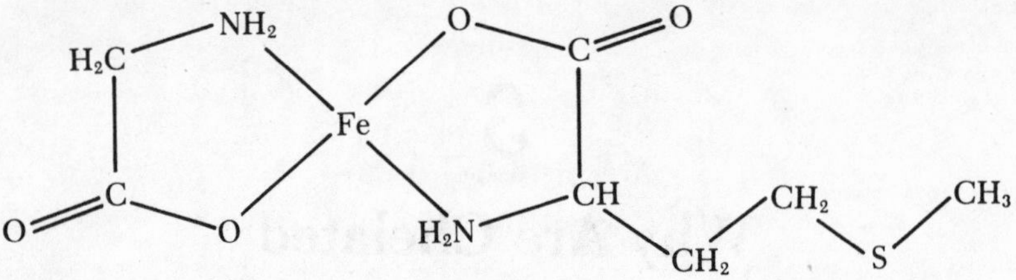

Figure 3 – 1. **A two-dimensional drawing of a bicyclic chelate with iron as the metal and glycine and methionine as sample amino acid ligands.**

The number of amino acids that can be joined to a metal atom is dependent on the oxidation state of the metal atom which is ultimately determined by the disposition of the electrons in the individual orbitals of the atom. Bicyclic (dipeptide-like) and tricyclic (tripeptide-like) molecules are typically formed. Even though the oxidation states of some metals would allow a fourth chelator, bonding angles and atomic distances required for chelation would generally preclude its occurrence much the same as the difficulty encountered in positioning four hands around the same marble.

Once a mineral has been chelated, the products composing the chelate are no longer amino acids or metal ions. They share similar properties with amino acids and metals, but also have several unique properties all their own. A mineral which has been correctly chelated tends to be absorbed in the intestine in a fashion similar to dipeptide and tripeptides, and is an entirely different concept than the absorption and metabolism of a nonchelated or improperly chelated mineral.

Chelation is a process essential to the formation of the multitude of enzyme systems that directly or indirectly control our bodies' metabolism. As discussed in the preceding chapter, enzymes are tiny chemical factories which reside inside and outside body cells. The enzymes are composed primarily of amino acids, vitamins, and minerals. Specific minerals are generally chelated into specific enzymes. Their presence activates the enzyme. When the mineral is absent, the enzyme won't work. Recently, scientists at Albion Laboratories have shown that, were it not for chelation, the synthesis of many of our life-dependent hormones would be impossible. For example, adrenotrophin, a hormone needed to meet stress conditions, cannot be produced unless there is adequate calcium and magnesium to stimulate the pituitary gland at the base of the brain. In the immune system, superoxide dismutase (SOD) activity is increased when copper, zinc, and manganese are chelated to special amino acids and then taken as a supplement. For the nutritionist, the most widely recognized role of chelation is in the intestinal absorption of essential minerals.

Because of that function, a great deal of attention has been concentrated on designing specific chelates which can be used by the body to enhance mineral absorption. In the recently published book *Intestinal Absorption of Metal Ions and Chelates*, the authors have summarized current research by scientists from around the world, which indicates that the small amount of nonchelated divalent minerals that may be absorbed by the body are naturally chelated or complexed in the stomach and intestinal tract or on the intestinal wall prior to entering the bloodstream and passing into the cell. However, the natural chelation of minerals in the stomach and intestines is not a simple process and is dependent upon a number of variables that must be in balance. The complexity of the chelation process can best be demonstrated by outlining the various steps necessary to move an inorganic mineral, known as a mineral salt, through the digestive process, into the bloodstream, and into the cell.

1. A mineral salt, such as iron sulfate, is swallowed and enters the stomach, where it is ionized, or the iron is broken apart from its carrier (sulfate), by going into solution. In simpler terms, it is dissolved.
2. Certain proteins, which must be present, are broken down to amino acids by the hydrolyzing effect of hydrochloric acid and other digestants, including enzymes.
3. With the proper change in pH, free amino acids are negatively charged and then attached to the positively charged mineral ions and form easily absorbable chelate molecules.

4. If the mineral ion remains unattached to either the amino acids or to the precipitants, which will prevent its absorption when it enters the intestinal tract, it can be chelated to specific proteins on the membrane of an intestinal cell and transferred into the body.

It is apparent that several key factors influence chelation. In order for the optimum chelation of the mineral ions to take place during the digestive process, the following conditions must be met:

1. The sources providing minerals and amino acids must be ingested at the same time.
2. Adequate digestive aids must be present to ionize the mineral salts and also break down the proteins to amino acids.
3. The amino acids must combine in a stable formation with the mineral, thereby chelating the mineral ion with amino acids derived from hydrolyzed protein. This process necessitates an abundance of certain amino acids.
4. The factors which almost always interfere with this chelation process must be eliminated or at least controlled. To illustrate just how complex the presence or absence of these factors is, consider the effects of certain substances on calcium bioavailability. Table 3-1 lists only a few.

Under ideal conditions, the chelation of most minerals occurs daily in the stomach and intestines. As evidenced by the growing deficiency of minerals found in the body, there is an apparent reduction of the chelation process for one reason or another. Perhaps we suffer from inadequate minerals in the diet, inadequate protein, or inadequate digestive elements. There may be too many substances present in the digestive system that will prevent chelation from occurring in the first place because they tie up the minerals and make them nonchelatable. Whatever the cause, any one of these problems can seriously affect the body's ability to make use of needed minerals.

Chelation is both directly and indirectly involved with nutrients as they move throughout the body since many of the body's tissues and organs cannot make use of these nutrients in a nonchelated form. Iron is moved throughout the body by

Table 3-1. Effect of Some Ligands on Calcium Bioavailability

Decrease	Increase	No Effect
Phytate	Lactose	Dietary
Fiber	Medium chain triglycerides	Protein
Oxalate	Vitamin D	Ascorbic acid
Fat	Amino acids	Citric acid
Alcohol		Pectin
Sodium alginate		
Uronic acid		
EDTA		
NTA		
Phosphorus		
Magnesium		

means of a complex amino acid chelate called apoferritin. Vitamin B_{12} is actually chelated cobalt. Chelation is also a factor in the body's defense against dangerous bacterial multiplication within the body. For example, a copper chelate of hydrazine has been effectively used as a bactericide because, through chelation, it withholds copper from the bacterial growth enzyme transaminase. Bacteria, like human body cells, have numerous enzyme systems that depend on minerals as the activating part of those enzymes. Chelation appears to be an essential part of the body's defense against viral invasions through production of superoxide dismutase (SOD).

Finally, chelation has proven to be one of the keys to those chemical forces which cause the binding, twisting, and turning of the protein molecules resulting in the DNA molecules endowed with the genetic patterns of life. Chelation is in fact the mechanism which furnishes the reactions that make possible the interrelated functioning of vitamins, amino acids, minerals, hormones, etc., that are essential for all the body's metabolic processes. Figure 3-2 shows a few of those relationships that have to do with energy breakdown and utilization.

In discussing the functions of chelation, frequently the

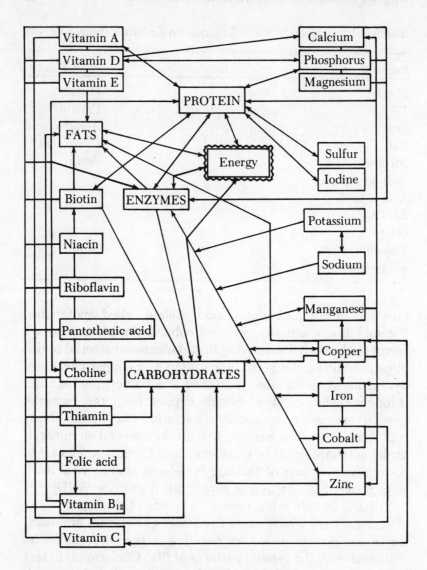

Figure 3 – 2. **The interrelationship of nutrients as they relate to energy production.** SOURCE: Courtesy of Albion Laboratories, Inc.

question is asked, "If chelation of minerals is so essential for life, what happens when we consume nonchelated or improperly chelated minerals?" I explain that the body cannot directly use most minerals until the minerals have been properly chelated with amino acids from hydrolyzed protein either inside or outside the body. If minerals are consumed in a nonchelated or improperly chelated form, the body must generally chelate or rechelate them in the stomach and/or intestines before the minerals can be absorbed into the bloodstream.

For example, suppose a person were to swallow chelated iron gluconate. Gluconates are made from a fermentation process using sugar, which makes the gluconates an unnatural substance in the digestive system. Thus, gluconate chelates are unable to attain maximum mineral absorption. In order to obtain the iron from this supplement, the body must first remove the gluconate from the iron through a chemical process called ionization. This separation occurs automatically as the iron gluconate is dissolved in the liquids present in the stomach. Once freed from the gluconate compound, the iron becomes unstable and can thus enter into any number of chemical reactions that naturally take place in the stomach and intestines. These reactions bind unstable minerals, such as iron, so tightly that they are no longer soluble and available for chelation and use by the body. Consequently, only a small percentage of the swallowed mineral from a gluconate or other improperly chelated mineral is absorbed through the intestines. The rest is eliminated as waste.

To illustrate the differences in absorption, Professor Alfred Soffer, a university professor as well as a medical doctor, has reported in his book on chelation that iron gluconate was no better absorbed than nonchelated iron sulfate and that certain other unnatural chelates were not even absorbed as well. On the other hand, research done at Albion Laboratories in conjunction with a prominent university has proven that when the [59]iron is *correctly* chelated with amino acids, the intestinal absorption of the [59]iron is many times greater than that for [59]iron sulfate, as seen in Table 3-2.

Table 3-2.   Mean Comparison of [59]Fe
Retention and Distribution

	cc/m/gm		
Body Part	[59]Iron Sulfate	[59]Iron Amino Acid Chelate	% Increase [Decrease] Chelate/Sulfate
Heart	63	151	140
Liver	136	243	79
Leg muscle	2	54	2,600
Jaw muscle	14	138	886
Brain	31	130	319
Kidney	2	327	16,250
Testes	20	109	445
Blood serum	700	1,797	157
Red blood cells	724	2,076	180
Whole blood	1,355	4,215	211
Feces	302,400	214,000	[29]

Data are shown as corrected counts per minute per gram of body portion being analyzed (cc/m/gm). SOURCE: Courtesy of Albion Laboratories, Inc.

Looking at the same problem from a more practical point of view, suppose we bought 100 tablets of iron sulfate or chelated iron gluconate and paid $6.00 for the bottle of tablets. Now let's open the bottle and throw away ninety-four of those tablets. Admittedly that would be wasteful, but that is basically what our body will do with 94 percent of the iron. The remaining six tablets represent what our body will normally absorb out of the 100 tablets when given that type of iron supplement. With other iron supplements, the absorption is even less. Research has shown that absorption of these types of iron is, at best, only about 6 percent, so when we paid $6.00 for the bottle of tablets, instead of costing 6 cents per tablet for the iron, based on absorption, it has actually cost us $1.00 per tablet. Such is the body's treatment of nonchelated mineral supplements.

For many of the same reasons mentioned earlier, improperly chelated minerals are nearly as wasteful as nonchelated minerals. This fact was illustrated in a letter from a scientist who had been using a certain commercial brand of amino acid chelated minerals for use in his research project. He told me in his letter that about halfway through the research project the chelated minerals stopped producing the same results in the people to whom he was giving them. "At first I couldn't figure out what was wrong," he wrote. "The minerals looked, smelled, and tasted the same as they always had, but they didn't work anymore. It took quite a bit of detective work, but the supplier of the supplements finally admitted that it had changed chelation manufacturers because the new chelate was cheaper for the supplier to buy. The supplier tried to assure me that the chelates were identical to the ones I had been using, but I knew differently, because they had failed to produce the same results."

Just because a mineral is labeled a chelate does not guarantee that it will be absorbed. As shown in the book *Intestinal Absorption of Metal Ions and Chelates*, the body will absorb chelates that meet certain criteria. When we swallow chelates that don't conform to these requirements, even though they may be chelates, they are rejected.

Research has shown that chelated minerals are so important to our health and well-being that many manufacturers of mineral supplements have rushed to the marketplace with their own brands of chelated minerals without doing any research to determine whether or not their methods of chelation will actually enhance the absorption of the mineral. Their only objective in producing the "new" type of mineral supplement is the little extra profit they expect from calling their product a chelate.

Unfortunately, the word chelation is not magic. Chelation does not guarantee mineral absorption because there are many more wrong ways to make a chelate than there are right ways. Even though mineral supplements may contain identical ingredients, different methods of processing those ingredients can produce chelates of varying quality and effectiveness.

These differences in processing might be compared to making a cake. A great chef and a mediocre cook can start with exactly the same ingredients. However, because of the superior knowledge, experience, and past research of the chef, he is able to produce a masterful dessert which tantalizes the palate of the most discriminating gourmet. The mediocre cook, on the other hand, uses the same ingredients to produce a cake so unappealing that it sits half-eaten in the bread box until it is thrown out.

These differences are readily apparent when different brands of chelated minerals are compared in controlled testing. For example, when two calcium chelates, each made with amino acids, were tested for absorption along with inorganic calcium, it was found that the one chelate was absorbed 53 percent more efficiently than the inorganic calcium while the other chelate was absorbed at a level 76 percent higher than the inorganic calcium. Why was there a difference in absorption? Just as in the example of the two cakes, even though the same ingredients were used to make each of the calcium chelates, one chelate was processed differently from the other, which resulted in a different absorption level. Even though both chelates contained the same amount of calcium, they reacted differently inside the body. Such a breakdown in absorption of the calcium could have disastrous effects on a woman who desperately needed supplemental calcium for osteoporosis, assuming calcium deficiencies are related to the disease.

In a university experiment using manganese it was demonstrated that when it had been properly chelated with amino acids from hydrolyzed protein it was absorbed 300 percent better than the best form of inorganic manganese tested, while a second chelated manganese made by a different process was only twice as effective as the inorganic form. The only reputed difference in the two chelated manganese products was the way they were made. Chemical analysis revealed that the ingredients in these two chelates were exactly the same.

I remember seeing a magazine advertisement some time ago which posed the question, "How much is your body worth?"

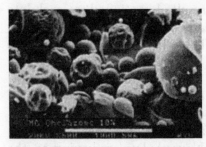

Figure 3 – 3. **Photographs taken with an electron microscope. The magnesium on the left is spherical in shape and a true chelate. The magnesium on the right is planar and simply an admixture of magnesium and protein. It is not a chelate.** SOURCE: Courtesy of Albion Laboratories, Inc.

That question has since caused me to reflect on the way some chelates are made and the value of some of these "chelated" minerals in providing mineral nutrition to the body. For example, some manufacturers take protein powder and mineral salts, mix them together, and call that a chelate. But since there has been no chemical reaction between the mineral and the chelating agent, the product is not a true chelate, and the absorption of the mineral by the body will be nil.

Other manufacturers in the mineral supplement industry go one step further in their attempts to produce a chelate. They wet the mixture of mineral salts and protein powder, dry the mixture, and call this a chelate. The mineral absorption from this product is not better than that of the first one mentioned. Another group of manufacturers may make use of some chemical reactions in the processing of their chelates, but upon looking for structural changes with an electron microscope, it becomes obvious that the raw ingredients remain as a simple mixture, and no chelation has occurred. It is easy to see which manufacturers simply make cheap mixtures and which manufacturers make true chelates as a result of sophisticated chemical reactions. Figure 3-3 compares separate magnesium chelates from two separate companies.

A final level of commercial manufacturer has produced

what I call a true chelate as a result of continued research into techniques to make better chelates and an incorporation of this research into their products. These processing techniques are sophisticated and expensive because they are designed to reproduce in manufacturing the type of chelate prepared naturally by the body. As the manufacturing techniques become more complex, the purity and quality of the ingredients become more critical, and, thus, the chelate becomes more expensive to produce. Nevertheless, returning to the original question "How much is your body worth?" it is certainly worth more than the price of a cheaply chelated mineral supplement that is of marginal value to the body. If your body is worth a mineral supplement at all, then it is worth a properly chelated mineral supplement that it can utilize fully.

Because a few of the chelated minerals are made in such a way as to provide a dramatic increase in mineral absorption, many people have expressed concern about getting an overdose. While some forms of chelated minerals do increase the chance of mineral toxicity, a lot depends on how naturally the chelate is processed. In other words, how closely does the manufacturing of the chelate conform to the way the body would build that same chelate under ideal conditions?

The question of toxicity revolves around the idea that ingestion of certain chemicals that are used in the growing or processing of foods is harmful to the body because of the abnormal reactions which these chemicals may cause.

The same problem is associated with nonchelated minerals. For example, magnesium sulfate, an inorganic form of magnesium, produces diarrhea. Iron sulfate can cause gastric upset—diarrhea or constipation—and should not be taken in the presence of vitamin E because of its destructive effect on that nutrient.

These toxic reactions do not occur if these same minerals which cause constipation, diarrhea, gastric upset, or other problems are ionized (removed from their carriers such as carbonate, sulfate, or gluconate) and properly chelated with amino acids from hydrolyzed protein. Frequently it is the carrier of the mineral and not the mineral itself that causes toxicity to the body.

On the other hand, a properly chelated mineral is a natural mineral. It is not a chemical additive and, consequently, its toxic effects on the body are practically nonexistent. This fact has been demonstrated in studies conducted at the University of Utah and published in the book *Chelated Mineral Nutrition in Plants, Animals, and Man.*

To illustrate this point, a few weeks ago I was lecturing at a symposium in Mexico. One of the other speakers was a college professor who was doing some toxicity experiments on a certain brand of chelated minerals. "I'm frustrated," he told me. "I can't kill the test animals with the brand of chelates with which I'm working. We know that copper can be one of the most lethal of all the normal trace elements to work with. Unfortunately, for my research, when we properly chelate the copper with amino acids from hydrolyzed protein it takes on different properties. I've inserted it directly into the stomachs of the animals until I can't force any more into the animal without rupturing the stomach, but I still can't kill the animals."

Outwardly I consoled the professor for his lack of success in determining a toxic level for that particular form of copper, while inwardly I was pleased to learn of the apparent safety of properly chelated minerals. This scientist's findings confirmed research done at the medical center of another university. In their published studies they reported that they could not kill the test animals when they forced calcium, magnesium, zinc, chromium, or manganese chelates into the stomachs of their test animals, provided that each of those metals was properly chelated with amino acids from hydrolyzed protein.

I recently reviewed the results of an experiment conducted in animals extending over several years using numerous generations. Pigs were selected as the test animals because of their physiological similarities to human beings. Pregnant females were fed specific chelated or nonchelated minerals throughout pregnancy. When the offspring were born they too continued to receive the same minerals as their mothers. As the female offspring matured and became pregnant the supplement process repeated itself through that generation and into the next. Five generations of animals were finally created which had received these various minerals all of their fetal and postnatal lives. An animal pathologist who examined the tissues from various generations concluded that there were no abnormalities in the tissues of pigs which received the chelated minerals. The tissues from those pigs receiving the chelated minerals were generally more healthy than the tissues of the pigs receiving the nonchelated minerals.

Why shouldn't these buffered and stabilized amino acid chelates be less toxic? Our bodies have been depending on them since the moment we were conceived and still in our mother's womb. Why shouldn't there be greater absorption of properly chelated minerals? They are as natural as the limited amounts of chelated minerals in the foods we eat and certainly more available. Our bodies don't have to digest them before absorption. Our bodies don't lose properly chelated minerals.

Realizing the importance of chelation to our lives, how do we tell which chelated minerals result in the types of natural benefits our bodies require? First, we should determine whether the mineral supplement we have selected has been chelated with either pure amino acids or amino acids from hydrolyzed protein. Being chelated with ascorbic acid, gluconate, or orotates (which have been reported to cause liver damage) or other chelating agents may not get the mineral through the intestines into the blood as an intact compound. Many of the amino acid chelates fail in this regard as well, so we should take a second step and ask manufacturers for scientific proof that their minerals are absorbed efficiently. We should not settle for anything short of verifiable, published research. Bona fide chelate manufacturers should be happy to provide research proving their claims of superior absorption, lower toxicity, etc.

It is evident that our bodies depend on chelated minerals in order to function. If our food contains insufficient quantities of these essential minerals, as government research quoted in previous chapters has indicated is often the case, then we must rely on supplements. If we supplement with nonchelated or incorrectly chelated minerals, our bodies will do their best to make the necessary conversions to accommodate what we have put into our stomachs. But if we force our bodies to do that additional work and, through no fault of the body, a mineral deficiency state results, we must not expect our bodies to function at the same level of efficiency that is possible when we have adequate body levels of these minerals in our tissues and cells. Neither can we expect our vitamins to work as well. Further, our protein, fat, or carbohydrate metabolisms will not be as efficient without adequate intake of minerals. When we put nonchelated minerals in our mouth there is no guarantee that they will be absorbed. When we don't obtain all of our needed minerals in a chelated form that we can use, the chances of our bodies achieving their full potential are significantly reduced.

ADDITIONAL READING

Harvey, S., *Minerals: Right on Target* (Orem: Nature's Field), 1987.

Ashmead, D., "Chelation in nutrition," *World Health and Ecology News*, 7:4, 1976.

Schutte, K., *The Biology of the Trace Elements* (Philadelphia: J.B. Lippincott Company), 1964.

Coffey, R., "The role of trace elements and minerals in problem cattle herds," *Modern Veterinary Practice*, April 1986.

Ashmead, H. D., *et al.*, *Intestinal Absorption of Metal Ions and Chelates* (Springfield: Charles C Thomas), 1985.

Kratzer, F. and Vohra, P., *Chelates in Nutrition* (Boca Raton: C.R.C. Press, Inc.), 1986.

Soffer, A., *et al.*, *Chelation Therapy* (Springfield: Charles C Thomas), 1964.

Ashmead, D., ed., *Chelated Mineral Nutrition in Plants, Animals, and Man* (Springfield: Charles C Thomas), 1982.

Ashmead, H., *et al.*, "Chelation does not guarantee mineral metabolism," *J. Appl. Nutrition*, 26:5, Summer 1974.

Jeppsen, R., *Assessment of long term feeding of chelated amino acid minerals (Metalosates®*) in sows (Clearfield: Albion Laboratories, Inc.), 1987.

Gallagher, C., *Nutritional Factors and Enzymological Disturbances in Animals* (Philadelphia: J.B. Lippincott Company), 1964.

4

Not All Chelates
Are Created Equal

A t a National Natural Foods Association convention in Las Vegas, owners and managers of health food stores all over the country heard several prominent authorities speak on many important subjects relating to nutrition. In addition to the fine speakers, the convention offered an exhibit hall where hundreds of manufacturers presented their nutritional or health-related products to the retailers.

Entering the huge exhibit hall containing countless dazzling displays, I met an old friend whom I had not seen for several months. After exchanging greetings and briefly bringing each other up to date on what had been happening, we decided to tour the exhibit together.

Because of my intense interest in minerals, we stopped at all the booths which sold mineral supplements to health food stores. At exhibit after exhibit we were told of the great advances in mineral chelation and assured that the supplements were guaranteed to increase mineral absorption and metabolism. Unaware of my background in chelation research, most of the salespeople went to great lengths to persuade my friend and me how vital chelated minerals were in improving our nutritional programs.

One salesperson referred us to a book entitled *Orthomolecular Nutrition* in which the authors wrote, "Chelation of a mineral is a natural step in the absorption and use of a mineral by the body. Minerals chelated with amino acids exist in nature. They combine naturally for absorption into our

37

systems via the digestive tract. When non – amino acid chelated minerals such as sulfates or gluconates reach the intestine, they are there chelated for absorption, if amino acids are available for a chelate to form. Amino acid chelated minerals help side-step this part of the digestive process because they are already bonded with amino acids."[1]

Later, as my friend and I visited at our hotel, he gave what he thought was a sincere compliment when he said, "Well, you've finally accomplished one of your lifelong goals, DeWayne."

"What do you mean?" I responded.

My friend smiled and said, "I know that your company has been involved in chelation since the early 1960s. You personally started speaking and publishing magazine articles on chelation in the early 1960s, although I believe that your research started much earlier. Soon, you began teaching doctors and nutritionists that absorption of inorganic minerals was low and inconsistent, and that by chelating these same minerals, their absorption and metabolism could be vastly improved."

"So, what are you getting at?" I asked. "What lifelong goal have I finally achieved?"

"Don't you see?" said my friend. "When you first started talking about chelation, no one believed you. Chelation was an unfamiliar term and little was known about the process in the health-care and nutrition communities. But you were per-sistent in your efforts to produce and present new research. Before long people started listening, universities started agreeing, and even skeptics were forced to accept the facts. I think that our experience today at the exhibits proves that most people have finally come out of the dark and realized that unless most minerals are chelated, absorption may be low and utilization by the body poorer."

"Most of the people here are still in the dark," I grumbled.

"What do you mean?"questioned my friend. "Knowing how concerned you've been over mineral nutrition, I should think you would be delighted to see so many companies finally adopting chelation as a necessary process in the production of their mineral supplements."

As I looked at my friend sitting on the sofa in my hotel room, I thought to myself, I wonder how many trusting people are consuming certain brands of mineral supplements simply because the manufacturer has put the word chelated on the label? "Morry," I replied slowly, "when you chelate a mineral, it means that you take each atom of that mineral, such as zinc, and make it soluble by ionizing it. While it is in the soluble state, you bond it to chelating agents, such as amino acids. To help stabilize the chelate through a complex patented process, the mineral is suspended between two amino acids. The effect is similar to two or more equally strong magnets suspending a ball bearing between them. In the case of chelation, the metal atom is suspended in the center of the chelating agents through a sharing and donating of electrons. As long as the mineral is suspended or surrounded by the chelating agents, the mineral remains more or less stable. Properly chelating a mineral is such a sophisticated and delicate process that I would be surprised if one out of ten of those companies at the convention today has the know-how to produce chelated minerals effectively, in spite of their label claims."

"So that's why you raised your eyebrows when that first salesperson told us that his zinc supplement was better for us because it was chelated."

"That's one of the chelates I was referring to when I said that a chelate may be more or less stable. The gluconate he was selling is a mineral that has been chelated with gluconic acid. This mineral supplement is not a natural chelate but a substance foreign to the body. Further, as a chelate, the gluconate is not as stable as the amino acid chelates the body forms, so it usually becomes unchelated in the stomach. In other words, it usually breaks apart long before it reaches the intestine where minerals are absorbed. When this happens, the unstable mineral which has been released by the gluconic acid is the same as an inorganic mineral, so its absorption is often as low as that of inorganic minerals.

"In fact, I remember one study in which investigators compared the absorption of iron gluconates to that of iron sulfate, an inorganic mineral whose intestinal absorption is about 6 percent. They found that chelated iron gluconate was not absorbed any better than iron sulfate. This research was published in medical journals as well as in a book on chelation. The latter was jointly authored by several medical doctors, biologists, and biochemists, all of whom are professors at leading universities. They concluded that one of the reasons gluconates are not effective nutritional supplements is because the gluconic acid that forms this type of chelate breaks down too rapidly. So you see, Morry, just because a company puts the word chelation on the label of their mineral product, that doesn't guarantee the mineral will be absorbed any better than inorganic minerals."

My friend thought for a moment and then continued, "You mentioned earlier that the chelates which are formed naturally in our bodies are generally composed of chelating agents containing amino acids from hydrolyzed protein. We saw several companies who claimed to have amino acid chelated minerals. Does this mean that they are the better brands to buy?"

"Anyone can claim to have amino acid chelates," I replied, "but in laboratory analysis of several of the amino acid chelates that are on the market, it was determined that many of them did not meet the criteria for being labeled a chelate. For example," I explained, reaching into my briefcase, "here is a fingerprint of a so-called iron amino acid chelate that was recently introduced in the market. This fingerprint or line graph is called an infrared spectrophotometer tracing. A complex instrument analyzes the mineral compound that is put into it and draws the line, or fingerprint, on the graph. The trained chemist then reads the graph and makes comparisons against chemically pure chelates. In analyzing this so-called iron amino acid chelate, its fingerprint showed that it was mostly iron phosphate. As you know, iron from iron phosphate cannot be absorbed because of its low solubility."

My friend studied the fingerprint I had shown him for a couple of minutes before concluding finally, "From what I see here, if you supplement your diet with this brand of amino acid chelates, you may get even less absorption than you would with the gluconic-acid chelates."

"You mean the gluconates," I added.

"Yes," he replied. "But does this mean that the manufactured amino acid chelates are not good either?"

"No, it doesn't mean that at all," I explained. "Some amino acid chelates are better than others, but the public doesn't know which will result in better absorption and which will not. What is disturbing is that many of the manufacturers who try to capitalize on the word chelation to sell their poorly absorbed minerals haven't done the research or perfected the processing which would enable them to manufacture a chelate that approximates the natural chelation process of the body."

"Then who does have enough experience to manufacture a true chelate?" my friend asked.

"Research scientists at Albion Laboratories have been studying chelation since 1962, and they have found that the absorption of the mineral is affected greatly by the type of protein used and the method of hydrolyzing it into amino acids. Some companies simply mix minerals with protein powder and call the product a chelate. Many companies don't even bother to digest the protein into amino acids.

"I remember talking to the chief chemist in the research department of a reputable company in Germany which had recently received a sample of a magnesium chelate from an American company which produced one of these pseudo-chelates. The German company took a magnifying glass and separated the magnesium oxide crystals into one pile and the protein powder into another pile. These scientists were appalled that this American company could be so unethical as to pass off the mixture of magnesium oxide and protein as a chelate.

"The manufacture of an amino acid chelate is complex even though the concept seems simple. Both the amino acids and minerals must be in solution. Uninformed manufacturers often think all they have to do is mix soggy protein with mineral powders, dry the paste, and then grind it up. These companies appear to not have the equipment, which costs millions of dollars, the technology, which takes years to develop, or the necessary materials, or they simply refuse to spend the extra money necessary to make a quality chelate."

"Is the method of hydrolyzing the protein the only difference between good and bad chelates?" questioned my friend.

In answering, I continued to explain the complex nature of chelation. "Absorption of chelated minerals is such a complex process that consideration must be given to production variables such as molecular size of the chelate, types of amino acids used, as well as other chelation techniques. According to Dr. Lee Tiffin of the US Department of Agriculture, when minerals are chelated with amino acids, the resulting molecule must have a molecular weight of less than 1,500 if the chelate is to be absorbed intact.

"I recall a research project in which the molecular weights of several chelates were measured. Every manufacturer except one had made chelates whose molecular weights were between 4,500 and 10,000. No one could make a smaller chelate because they would have infringed on the patent of the only company whose chelates had a molecular weight less than 1,000. In other words, to my knowledge only one company is building amino acid chelates that can be absorbed by the body intact. The other products, if they are chelates at all, must be digested in the stomach and intestines before they can be absorbed. When digestion occurs and generally releases the minerals from the chelating agent, these free metal ions are no better absorbed than nonchelated minerals.

"Further, if a chelate is not stabilized during the manufacturing process, it will break apart in the stomach and release the metal even if it is an amino acid chelate. This negates any benefit that may have once been possible from the chelate. In order to stabilize the chelate the pH of the solution in which the chelate is being made must be precisely controlled throughout the manufacturing process. When that process is followed then the chelate will be absorbed."

"How do you know?" my friend asked.

I told him about some research with cattle in which glass windows were surgically implanted in their rumens so that scientists could observe their digestive processes and remove the rumen material from time to time to see if the action of the enzymes, acids, and rumen bacteria had destroyed the chelate. Cattle were chosen as the test animals because the chelates remained in their four stomachs much longer than in the single stomachs of humans and therefore the environment the chelate was subjected to was much harsher. If it worked in a cow, it would work in humans. These university scientists found that when the chelate was stabilized under a patented process, it not only survived the harsh environment of the stomach and did not break apart, but it was also absorbed in greater amounts than other chelates.

"Albion Laboratories is the only company in the industry with patents guaranteeing that, if the mineral is chelated, it will result in greater absorption of that mineral. If you look closely at labels, you will see that no other company even claims that its chelates are absorbed except Albion. These companies don't make these claims because of possible patent infringements or lack of research proof that their products are truly better than inorganic mineral salts."

"The whole process sounds complicated," said my friend.

"It is," I agreed. "Let me show you some other infrared spectrophotometer fingerprints," I added, reaching into my briefcase and pulling out some of the infrared spectrophotometer tracings. "These are fingerprints of two iron chelates which have been compared to an iron amino acid chelate fingerprint produced by the body. As you can see, the one chelate which was produced correctly is similar to the chelated iron found in the liver. It was manufactured only after taking into account all the problems I mentioned earlier. The other purported amino acid chelate, as far as I know, is not backed by any research. Consequently, as the graph shows, it fails to conform to the standard of the natural chelate found in the body." (See Figure 4-1.)

Just then my telephone rang. It was the owner of another

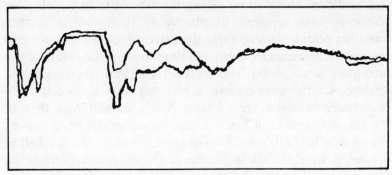

True Iron Amino Acid Chelate

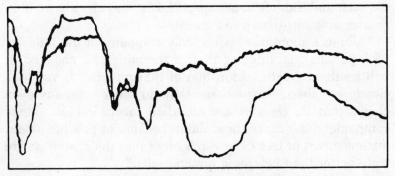

Imitation Iron Amino Acid Chelate

Figure 4 – 1. **Infrared spectrophotometer tracings of liver iron compared to two iron amino acid chelates. The darker lines are the iron amino acid chelates found in the liver.** Source: Courtesy of Albion Laboratories, Inc.

company, who had made an appointment with me earlier. He was interested in learning more about chelation so he, in turn, could educate his customers. I invited him to join us.

While we were waiting for him to arrive, my friend asked, "When consumers buy chelated minerals, how can they be certain they are buying a chelate that can be absorbed?"

"There are several things consumers can do," I answered. "They should not necessarily look for the cheapest product. Production of a true chelate that can be absorbed effectively by the body is an expensive process. I am acquainted with a leading vitamin company that had tested a certain patented mineral chelate in its own laboratory. The sales manager told me that this product was better than any chelate they had ever tested and certainly better than the product they were currently selling in the same market. When I asked him why his company didn't start selling the new chelate he said, 'Because it's more expensive.' He then confided to me that even though his company had developed a good reputation through their advertising for selling quality products, the company was really interested only in its sales volume and its profits. To sell an expensive chelate, even if it was the only one that was actually absorbed, would mean less profit because the competition would continue selling cheap chelates. His company would not sacrifice profits for quality."

"But even if I pay a good price for the product," questioned my friend, "how can I be assured of getting a quality chelate?"

"I usually tell people to read the label carefully," I answered. "Most chelates that we have tested in our laboratories or which have been tested by independent laboratories which meet the criteria for absorption and metabolism contain a patent number on the label. This means that the person or company obtaining the patent had to prove to the U.S. Patent Office that he or she had discovered a new product. In the case of nutritional supplements, it may have been necessary to prove efficacy, lack of toxicity, superior metabolism, and other qualities of the product. Research data on the new product should be available to the consumer. A reputable manufacturer will generally have good scientific research to back up claims that the chelates are compatible with the body, while product imitators usually have no research. A consumer can ask for a copy of the original research data, which usually accompanies promotional material on a quality product.

"I believe that in the future, the Food and Drug Administration may require metabolism and other bioavailability studies on all nutritional products, which will be a welcome regulation for an industry which has seen so many mediocre products flood the market recently."

NOTES

1. A. Hoffer and M. Walker, *Orthomolecular Nutrition* (New Canaan: Keats Publishing, 1978), p. 151.

ADDITIONAL READING

Hoffer, A. and Walker, M., *Orthomolecular Nutrition* (New Canaan: Keats Publishing), 151, 1978.

Ashmead, H., "Trace minerals—There is a difference," paper presented at National Health Federation annual meeting, Salt Lake City, August 1973.

Soffer, A., *et al.*, *Chelation Therapy* (Springfield: Charles C Thomas), 1964.

Ashmead, H., *et al.*, "Chelation does not guarantee mineral metabolism," *J. Appl. Nutri.*, 26:5, Summer 1974.

Tiffin, L., "Translocation of micronutrients," in Dinaeur, R., ed., *Micronutrients in Agriculture* (Madison: Soil Science Society of America, Inc.), 199, 1972.

Ashmead, D. H., "The need for nutrient bioavailability standards," paper given at Bioavailability 88 Conference, Norwich, England, August 1988.

Kratzer, F. and Vohra, P., *Chelates in Nutrition* (Boca Raton: CRC Press, Inc.) 1986.

Beede, D., "Artificial rumen study," Publication pending, 1989.

5

Mineral Targeting
Through Chelation

H ave you ever seen this?" a business associate asked as he
entered my office with an old magazine.

I looked at the article he had found while he was rummag-
ing through back issues of the magazines looking for something
else. The article had been written by a former employee who
had published a lot of my research data after leaving my
employment. At the time the data were published I was dis-
turbed because he reported them as if the research had been
done by his current employer. It had been almost ten years
since I had seen the article and yet as soon as my business
associate showed it to me a flood of old memories returned.

Glancing at the article I indicated that I was aware of it and
in brief terms told my colleague where the research had
originated.

He nodded and said, "Yes, I thought it had a familiar ring."
Then he pointed to a specific portion of the article and asked,
"But what about this?"

I reread the portion he was referring to. The author was
talking about how to make a chelated mineral in general
terms. He stated that when a chelate is made, the manufacturer
should avoid using any raw ingredient that would interfere with
the absorption of the mineral. In the article he explained that
sometimes manufacturers add ingredients to the chelate before
or after the product is made which will affect the way the
chelate behaves in the body.

As I reread this portion of the article I recalled how this in-

47

dividual had been on the research team that discovered that there were numerous ways to make an amino acid chelate but that not all techniques guaranteed absorption. In fact, if certain manufacturing processes were used to make amino acid chelates the resulting product was not absorbed, even though it was a chelate.

As I sifted through my memories of those exciting days of new discoveries I was brought back to the present with the question "I wonder what that author would say today if he knew that the research he was involved in at Albion would some day lead to the discovery of targeted chelates?"

I too wondered. A decade ago we knew we could move more of a mineral to one part of the body by changing the manufacturing techniques, but we couldn't get enough mineral deposition in a tissue or organ to make a significant difference.

Then came a discovery that changed all that. We learned how to make pure amino acid chelates. In the past, manufacturers had used hydrolyzed protein for the amino acid portion of their chelates. Some companies hydrolyzed the protein down to the amino acid state. Others did not. But in either case there were residues left that could potentially interfere with the uptake of the mineral and its migration to different parts of the body.

"That's why certain people couldn't take a soy-based chelate, while others couldn't tolerate a casein- or albumen-based chelate, and still others wanted a rice-based chelate," my associate told me. "They were having an allergic reaction to the residues in those amino acid sources."

"That's right," I agreed. "But now we have found a commercial way to make pure amino acid chelates which do not have the hydrolysis residues in them."

I then reminded him of the changes we had made in the mineral portion of the chelate. In the past manufacturers had used salts, such as iron sulfate, as their source of the mineral. If they made a true chelate the iron sulfate, in this example, would be dissolved, which resulted in the iron being released from the sulfate and free to bond to the amino acids. But no one knew how to get rid of the sulfate portion of the raw ingredient, so it remained in the chelated product as a contaminant.

But no more. Our research people had learned how to purify the metal portion so that the resulting chelate was composed of a pure amino acid and pure metal ion. When this new chelate was administered to laboratory animals we discovered something entirely new. The chelate did not behave as amino acid chelates in the past had done. Its absorption was higher, but that was to be expected. The surprise was that because there was no absorption interference, the metal could be concentrated in a specific part of the body. Even more exciting was the fact that our scientists learned that by altering the amino acid configuration in addition to changing bonding strengths of the metals to each of the amino acids, the resulting chelate could be targeted to different parts of the body. This opened up a whole new field in mineral nutrition!

I reminded my associate that these new amino acid chelates were small molecules. Their molecular weights were as low as 298, which made them tiny when compared to other chelates on the market, which had molecular weights that ranged from 1,570 to 91,747. "The small molecular weight allows them to be absorbed through the intestine intact and into the bloodstream without being broken apart like other chelates," I said. "Thus the amino acid chelate we design in the laboratory is able to migrate to the target area of the body because the body doesn't reconstruct it into something else.

"The fact that the chelate is substantially pure reduces interference to absorption, as was alluded to in the article," I added. "But we have discovered that purity also allows the chelate to be targeted."

"Give me an example of what you mean," said my associate.

"OK," I answered. "As you know, the thyroid gland produces thyroxin, a hormone that stimulates metabolism to burn body fat. The thyroid gland is controlled by hormones produced in the pituitary gland located at the base of the brain. TRH (thyrotropin hormone) from the hypothalamus helps stimulate the pituitary gland. One of the minerals which will activate the pituitary gland and cause it to stimulate the thyroid gland is manganese chelated into a special amino acid combination.

"Knowing this, we designed an experiment in which pure [54]manganese was chelated to specific pure amino acids in such a way as to duplicate part of the TRH hormone, which activates the pituitary gland. This chelated [54]manganese was administered to experimental animals and the activity compared to nonchelated [54]manganese. In a two-hour period the [54]manganese level in the pituitary glands increased 20 percent. There was no increase in the inorganic [54]manganese group during the first hour. It increased only 12 radioactive corrected counts per minute per milligram of tissue in the next hour. Compare that to the chelate-administered group where the one-hour level was 25 radioactive corrected counts per minute per milligram of tissue and increased 100 percent in the next hour."

"What does it matter if you can target manganese to the pituitary and activate the thyroid gland?" he asked.

"It means greater body fat burning ability," I explained. "The T3 and T4 thyroid levels increased, which suggests greater thyroid activity. In other experiments this was confirmed. Laboratory animals were placed in metabolic chambers which measured their energy usage of ingested food. The group of animals receiving the nonchelated manganese burned 47.2 kilocalories of oxygen per square meter per hour whereas the chelate group burned 55.4 kilocalories of oxygen per square meter per hour."

Pulling out his calculator and punching in some numbers my associate announced, "That's a 17 percent increase in metabolic activity when the manganese is targeted."

"Yes," I answered and proceeded to tell him about groups of pigs that were studied for over a year. They were fed various manganese supplements. Nothing happened to their fat levels until they were fed the manganese amino acid chelate. Within two weeks the depth of their back fat had dropped almost 10 percent. When they were butchered, 89 percent of the chelated group was graded AA1 whereas only 56 percent of the other group received the same top grading. Since both groups of pigs were the same breed and had received the same diet except for the manganese chelate, the better-quality meat had to be due to this special manganese chelate. The higher grading was based on the lower amount of fat in the meat.

"What about targeting other minerals to other body tissues and organs?" he asked.

"At present we don't have all the answers," I admitted. "But we are still working on them. We know how to make iron bypass the liver and go directly to the spleen where it is immediately sent to the bone marrow to make new hemoglobin molecules sooner and in higher quantities than inorganic iron. We have been able to bring animals that could not conceive into estrus, with resulting conception. In human clinical studies we have found that targeted magnesium will lower blood pressure. And the research goes on."

"That's exciting," my associate said. Then glancing back at the article that initiated our conversation, he said, "I wonder if your former employee ever realized just how far the research would go into pure chelates when he wrote this article?"

"That's a question I don't think either of us can answer," I said smiling. Then I changed the subject.

ADDITIONAL READING

Harvey, S., *Minerals: Right on Target* (Orem: Nature's Field), 1987.

Ashmead, H. D., *et al.*, *Intestinal Absorption of Metal Ions and Chelates* (Springfield: Charles C Thomas), 1985.

Graff, D., "Radioactive isotope research with chelated minerals," in Ashmead, D., ed., *Chelated Mineral Nutrition in Plants, Animals, and Man* (Springfield: Charles C Thomas), 275, 1982.

Ashmead, H., "Manganese and Zinc Chelazone® and weight control," research report, July 1987.

Ashmead, H., "Zinc Chelazone® and the male sex organs," research report, July 1987.

Atherton, D., "Summary of chelate evaluation trials," *Bibby Pig Technical Bulletin*, April 1985.

Manspeaker, J. *et al.*, "Chelated minerals: Their role in bovine fertility," *Vet. Medicine*, 951, September 1987.

Ashmead, D., "Oral supplementation of Fe and Zn in pigs," *Modern Vet. Practice*, 64:69, January 1983.

Atherton, D., "Evaluation of Manganese Metalosate® and Chelazome®," research report, November 1988.

Mordenti, A., "An evaluation of Manganese Metasolate® in Finishing Pigs," Publication pending, 1988.

Mordenti, A., "Research on the efficiency of Manganese Chelazome® as a dietary additive," Publication pending, 1989.

6

The Relationship of Minerals to Health and Disease

About five years ago, my mother's little dachshund, Rosy, had a severe stroke. My mother was understandably distraught since Rosy had been a part of the family for years and was now almost completely paralyzed. The veterinarian who attended Rosy suggested that the dog be put to sleep. It seemed the only humane thing to do.

But my mother refused, insisting, "Rosy has been with me too many years to be put to sleep. She doesn't want to die any more than you do."

"But look at her," the veterinarian reasoned. "She can't even stand up to get at her food and water, let alone walk outside by herself. It would be better for the dog if she were put to sleep." Then he added, "Rosy will never get any better."

In spite of these arguments, my mother's wishes prevailed. The dog was taken home even though she couldn't walk and could hardly lift her head. Picking the animal up apparently caused excruciating pain, so Rosy was carefully placed onto a two-foot-square board and then carried where she needed to go.

At first Rosy was force-fed, but later she was able to eat and drink without assistance. In addition to her regular food, my mother gave Rosy high levels of specially chelated minerals, minerals which many researchers have shown are more compatible with the bodies of animals as well as the human body and therefore absorbed and metabolized in much higher quantities.

At first the minerals had no noticeable effect on Rosy. Then

53

one day she lifted her head and seemed to show some interest in her surroundings. About four weeks later, Rosy slowly pulled herself up and stood on her four shaky legs. After taking two or three steps, she collapsed, but was soon up again trying to steady herself. As the weeks went by, Rosy became stronger, and soon she was walking around the house. Shortly thereafter Rosy indicated that she wanted to go outside by herself. When the door was opened, Rosy bounded down the three steps and out into the yard. Later my mother heard Rosy scratching at the back door. She had hopped up the three steps onto the porch and was waiting to come back in. In time, Rosy became frisky. She lived several more years before finally succumbing to old age at the human equivalent of over 100 years.

When he saw the change in Rosy, the veterinarian who had attended the dog was amazed at her recovery from the stroke. He conceded that the special mineral nutrition had played a major role in Rosy's rejuvenation, but he couldn't explain the reasons for it.

Since the veterinarian was a personal friend, I sat down with him and offered what I thought was the reason the minerals had been so effective with Rosy. "To understand the importance of mineral nutrition to health," I explained, "let us analyze why various parts of the body depend on minerals."

"I'd be interested to know more about minerals," said the doctor.

"My mother's dog, Rosy," I continued, "is much like you and me in the combination of physiological systems which make up her body. One of these many systems is the digestive system, which is composed of a number of organs including the mouth, esophagus, stomach, intestine, pancreas, liver, and gall bladder. Each organ in the system is made up of various tissues such as muscles, connective tissue, epithelial tissue, and nerves. Ultimately, each tissue is composed of various cells. For example, the epithelial tissue is made up of argentaffin cells, goblet cells, paneth cells, and absorptive cells.

"As you know, each type of cell in your body has a specific

function. When the billions of body cells each carry out their assigned roles, they work together to create a living being.

"If we examine those cells under the microscope, we will discover that each one of them is only about 1/3000 of an inch in diameter. That means approximately 600 trillion cells work together to build an average adult. As each second of your life passes, 50 million cells throughout your body die and are replaced by new cells, provided your nutrition is adequate to support regeneration. You see, billions of cells in your body live out their useful lives and die in amazingly short periods of time.

"The human body is so complex that most cells, despite being varied in structure, depend on one another to carry out their individual functions. Each minute cell carries out a number of continuous chemical processes within its structure. In fact, each cell may be thought of as a chemical factory which utilizes enzymes to bring about the chemical reactions. In a single cell, for example, there may be up to 50,000 enzyme units. These different enzymes cause a multitude of chemical reactions within the cell, keeping the cell and ultimately the whole body alive. Indeed, it has been estimated that as many as 50,000 enzyme reactions may take place in certain cells each minute."

The veterinarian glanced at his watch. "I appreciate the short course in physiology," he said impatiently, "but you still haven't told me what all this has to do with mineral nutrition."

"I was just getting to that," I explained. "A large number of enzymes within the cells cannot work alone. They need an activator, which in most cases is a specific mineral. For example, in the liver cells there is an enzyme called butyryl dehydrogenase. This enzyme breaks down fats into simpler units. But it won't digest fats down into simple units unless copper is present to activate the enzyme; one of the enzymes involved in making muscle and skin protein from amino acids requires manganese. Carbohydrate metabolism in the body cannot take place unless molybdenum activates a specific enzyme. In red blood cells, oxygen is brought in and carbon dioxide is given off only if the enzyme carbonic anhydrase is present, and zinc must activate that enzyme.

"Many of these enzymes are vital for life. If they are inhibited for even a short time a person could die. For example, the transmission of nerve impulses along the nerve sheath to and from the brain takes place only when acetylcholine chemically bridges the gap from nerve cell to nerve cell. The enzyme cholinesterase must then remove the excess acetylcholine or the nerve impulse repeats over and over. If you come in contact with certain insecticides, the enzyme is prevented from functioning, and a nerve block will occur. This is followed rapidly by death due to paralysis of the respiratory center. That's why the insecticide kills. The poison cyanide can kill because it combines with the iron in the heme enzyme and permanently blocks that enzyme's activity. This enzyme is needed to help carry oxygen throughout the body. The iron can no longer activate the enzyme in hemoglobin because it is tied up, resulting in death from suffocation."

I went on to explain to the veterinarian that the role of specific minerals in activating specific enzymes is a complex subject. "For example," I explained, "in his book *The Biology of the Trace Elements*, Karl Schute lists 202 identified enzymes that are influenced by minerals. Since 1964 when this book was published, scientists have discovered a multitude of new enzymes that require specific minerals in order to function. In many instances, if the activating mineral is absent or is replaced by another mineral, the enzyme will not function. And in many instances, if that specific enzyme doesn't work, the results can be fatal. On the other hand, if death doesn't result from enzyme blockage, a variety of health problems can develop."

"But wouldn't those kinds of drastic consequences only occur in situations where a mineral is completely absent in the system?" questioned my friend.

"Not according to current research," I responded, referring to another book from my library. "In their five-volume treatise *Mineral Metabolism*, Doctors Comar and Bronner reported that some diseases are characterized by only slight alterations in the concentration of specific minerals in the fluids surrounding the billions of body cells. Because the movement of minerals in and out of the cells is based on the mineral composition of the extracellular fluids, the mineral levels of these fluids can affect the mineral composition inside the cell where many of the enzymes work. These scientists reported that small departures from the normal mineral composition within the body cells may result in many different types of diseases without making any appreciable difference in the mineral makeup of the body as a whole. Statistically you would not be able to measure a difference."

"Data which make these minute changes in cellular levels even more alarming are shown in the physiological reactions of the body when a microorganism causes illness. Iron and zinc as well as amino acids are removed from the blood and sequestered where they are unavailable. Ultimately a negative balance of many minerals occurs as the disease progresses. [See Figure 6-1.] Because of these natural physiological reactions, the need for good mineral nutrition in a disease state is paramount."

I expanded on the topic of mineral balance by telling my veterinarian friend about a research project that Albion Laboratories and the University of Maryland have been carrying on for several years. "We found that many female animals were unable to conceive because of minute differences in the mineral levels in their reproductive organs. When these animals were examined using normal medical and clinical means, they did not show any mineral deficiencies or abnormalities. However, when tissue biopsies were taken and examined by an electron microscope with corresponding X ray dispersive microanalysis readings, mineral differences became apparent between the normal animals and those that could not conceive.

Based on these findings, Albion Laboratories developed special chelates that were absorbed in high quantities and targeted so that they were transported directly to the cells that make up the reproductive organs of the female animals. The

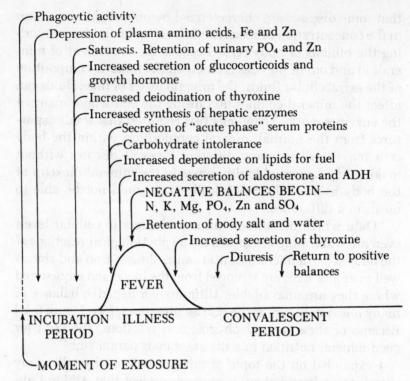

Phagocytic activity
Depression of plasma amino acids, Fe and Zn
Saturesis. Retention of urinary PO_4 and Zn
Increased secretion of glucocorticoids and growth hormone
Increased deiodination of thyroxine
Increased synthesis of hepatic enzymes
Secretion of "acute phase" serum proteins
Carbohydrate intolerance
Increased dependence on lipids for fuel
Increased secretion of aldosterone and ADH
NEGATIVE BALNCES BEGIN— N, K, Mg, PO_4, Zn and SO_4
Retention of body salt and water
Increased secretion of thyroxine
Diuresis
Return to positive balances
FEVER
INCUBATION PERIOD
ILLNESS
CONVALESCENT PERIOD
MOMENT OF EXPOSURE

Figure 6 – 1. **Host nutritional responses to infection.** SOURCE: W. Beisel, *Am. J. Clin. Nutr.,* 30:1236, 1977.

increased absorption and targeting of the minerals resulted in minute changes in the mineral composition of key cells, which was just enough change to allow conception to occur. Animals that had been unable to conceive now became pregnant or were delivering offspring. This research proved to be such a major breakthrough in reproductive physiology that the scientists at the University of Maryland who worked with Albion Laboratories on the project were invited to present their research findings at scientific and medical conventions all over the world."

"Do you suppose that mineral deficiencies play a greater part in diseases than we realize?" questioned my friend.

"It should be emphasized," I said, as my friend settled back in his chair, "that while some diseases and abnormalities are directly related to a mineral deficiency, such as iron deficiencies and anemia, most diseases are indirectly related. In other words, when the right minerals are present to activate correctly the cellular enzymes in their proper sequences, the body usually has a natural defense mechanism which is able to overcome or resist the effects of most causative disease agents. Thus, mineral deficiencies are not always the direct cause of a health problem, even though the deficiencies may set up conducive conditions for that illness."

"Could you give an example of how a mineral deficiency might make a person more susceptible to an illness?" questioned the doctor.

"Iron is a perfect example," I responded. "Iron in sufficient quantities prevents iron deficiency anemia and assists in the activation of a specific enzyme that helps make white blood cells, which, in turn, attack and destroy invading infections and infectious diseases. If body iron levels are low or even lacking in the tissue area where the white blood cells are made, specific enzymes cannot be activated and production of white blood cells is hindered. If this happens when an infectious disease has invaded the body, the consequences could be fatal. In 1976, Dr. Hal Hopson and I reported in a medical journal a study entitled "Iron Deficiencies and Their Relationship to Infectious Diseases." We demonstrated that a significant relationship existed between the amount of iron in the tissues and the incidence of disease.

"In a book entitled *Modern Nutrition in Health and Disease*, Doctors Goodhart and Shils point out that not all mineral disorders result in specific and characteristic clinical signs or pathological changes which are easily recognized, even by a competent physician. This is especially true when the disorder is mild. There are many variable factors including age and sex, the timing, duration and severity of the mineral deficiency, and the nature of the other elements or constituents of the diet.

"The authors also state that many of us do not absorb adequate amounts of a needed mineral even though it is found in the diet. Even after the minerals are absorbed, the body often fails to synthesize them into biologically active components for enzyme systems. Another factor contributing to low absorption is excessive excretion of minerals by the body. In research done in conjunction with Weber State College, we have found that a high percentage of nonchelated or improperly chelated minerals were returned to the lower bowel after absorption. The body couldn't metabolize the minerals even after they had been absorbed. On the other hand, when the same minerals were correctly chelated, absorption was found to be higher and retention of the minerals was significantly greater. The body could metabolize the properly chelated minerals because they were in a form that was totally natural.

"Remember that not all chelates, even some amino acid chelates, are totally natural. If an amino acid chelate is not anion-free, it is not natural. For example, if a chelate is made from iron sulfate and the sulfate is not removed from the resulting product, even though the iron portion may be chelated, the sulfate will act as the anion and will tend to interfere with complete absorption and metabolism of the iron. Based on chemical analysis of different products, most companies who sell chelates don't know how to remove the anions, or if they do know how, they are unwilling to go to the trouble of removing them. Consequently, these companies provide a contaminated chelate, one which is neither pure nor natural.

"In a series of experiments conducted by two professors from two separate universities and myself, we gave pigs oral doses of radioactive iron in different forms including the pure amino acid chelate form. We then traced the paths of the absorbed irons from the products. The pure chelate was absorbed in greater quantities, presumably because it was more natural.

"The interesting part of the experiments was what happened to the irons after they reached the bloodstream. The iron that was not chelated or was improperly chelated went to the livers of the test animals, where it was stored. Eventually, some of this iron was removed and sent to the bone marrow where new red blood cells were made. On the other hand, most of the pure chelated iron, upon reaching the blood, was sent to the spleen. The main purpose of the spleen is to extract the iron from dead red blood cells and return that iron to the bone marrow to make new red blood cells. The spleen evidently treats this pure chelate exactly the way it treats the iron it removes from dead red blood cells. The pure iron amino acid chelate was sent to the bone marrow where it became part of new red blood cells hours before the other irons that were sent to the liver became incorporated into hemoglobin. The purity of the chelate and its compatibility with the body affected the way the body responded to it."

"Then what you're saying is that we are not products of what we eat but what we absorb, retain, and use," said the doctor.

"I only wish more people understood that concept," I mused, shifting in my chair. "It may have been possible at one time to get adequate mineral nutrition from a balanced diet, but today many of our foods are minerally depleted. It is interesting to note that foods differ from crop to crop in their mineral contents. For example, spinach, a vegetable long thought to be high in iron, can vary in iron content from as many as 1,584 parts per million to as few as 19 parts per million, according to research done at Rutgers University. Even if the iron is present, Professor W. Van Dokkum reported at the Bioavailability 88 conference in England that the body still couldn't extract that iron from the spinach due to other constituents in the food that interfere with its absorption.

"Many feel the answer to balanced mineral consumption is in mineral supplements. But even swallowing numerous pills or capsules doesn't assure mineral absorption. There are many specific problems or barriers, including the mineral balance, oxidation state of the mineral, metal-ligand complex, type of mineral compound, other substances in the food, etc., which may reduce the amount of minerals we are able to absorb from our intestines. These barriers [some of which have been men-

tioned in earlier chapters in this book] can effectively prevent
absorption of the minerals by altering the intestinal environment and rendering it unfavorable for mineral availability.
Research at Albion Laboratories has confirmed that the majority of the minerals most people swallow leave the body as part
of the waste, having done little to nourish the tissues and cells
which are so dependent upon minerals for proper functioning.

"Realizing that there is a very real possibility that the
minerals swallowed are not absorbed, many people have turned
to chelation of those minerals as the answer. Unfortunately, as
noted earlier, this may not solve the problem either, since the
word chelation does not guarantee mineral absorption. Many
mineral supplements, although chelated, are not chelated in a
manner that allows the body to use them. This means that absorption of certain noncompatible amino acid chelates may be
lower than many nonchelated minerals, as university research
has shown. On the other hand, research by many investigators
has shown that when a mineral is chelated in a specific way,
then mineral metabolism usually increases because the mineral
is properly protected from the absorption barriers and absorbed
at different sites on the intestine. I have written an entire book
on that subject entitled *Intestinal Absorption of Metal Ions
and Chelates*.

"Other investigators have found that when these correctly
chelated minerals were supplemented to diseased animals having
specific mineral deficiencies, their responses to that type of supplementation were much more positive when compared to responses from other forms of the same mineral supplementation.

"In 1975, Professor Valkovic wrote that, excluding structural requirements, the majority of the minerals in our bodies
serve chiefly as activating components of our enzyme system.
He noted that if the mineral is removed from the enzyme, the
enzyme usually loses its capacity to function."

"These findings are quite convincing and far-reaching in their
implications," said my friend.

"I certainly don't mean to imply that every disease known
to man can be traced to a mineral disorder," I added.

"Perhaps research will some day shed more light on that idea. I believe that research into mineral nutrition will pay great dividends toward the health and well-being of mankind."

ADDITIONAL READING

De Robertis, E., *et al.*, *Cell Biology* (Philadelphia: W.B. Saunders Co.), 1975.

Milton, R., *Basic Nutrition and Cell Nutrition* (St. Catharines: Provoker Press), 1970.

Ashmead, H., "Tissue transportation of organic trace minerals," *J. Appli. Nutri.*, 22:42, Spring 1970.

Schutte, K., *The Biology of the Trace Elements* (Philadelphia: J.B. Lippincott Co.), 1964.

Ashmead, H., "Trace minerals—There is a difference," paper presented at National Health Federation annual meeting, Salt Lake City, August 1973.

Goodhart, R. and Shils, M., eds., *Modern Nutrition in Health and Disease* (Philadelphia: Lea & Febiger), 1980.

Schneider, H., *et al.*, eds., *Nutritional Support of Medical Practice* (New York: Harper & Row), 1977.

Comar, C. and Bronner, F., eds., *Mineral Metabolism* (New York: Academic Press), 5 volumes, 1960.

Prasad, A., ed., *Trace Elements in Human Health and Disease* (New York: Academic Press), 2 volumes, 1976.

Manspeaker, J., *et al.*, "Chelated minerals: Their role in bovine fertility," *Vet. Medicine*, 951, September 1987.

Coffey, R., "Predisposition to disease: The unknown factors," *Animal Health*, 10, October, 1985.

Hopson, H. and Ashmead, D., "Iron deficiencies and their relationship to infectious disease," *Vet. Med./Small Animal Clinic.*, 71:809, 1976.

Ashmead, D., "Oral Supplementation of Fe and Zn in Pigs," *Modern Vet. Practice*, 64:69, January, 1983.

Firman E. Bear Report, "Variations in mineral content in vegetables," Rutgers University.

Ashmead, H.D., *et al.*, *Intestinal Absorption of Metal Ions and Chelates* (Springfield: Charles C Thomas), 1985.

64   *Conversations on Chelation and Mineral Nutrition*

Valkovic, V., *Trace Element Analysis* (London: Taylor Francis Ltd.), 1975.

Kharasch, N., ed., *Trace Metals in Health and Disease* (New York: Raven Press), 1979.

Van Dokkum, W., "The significance of speciation for predicting mineral bioavailability," paper presented at Bioavailability 88 conference, Norwich, England, August 1988.

Ashmead, H.D., *et. al.*, "A peptide dependent intestinal pathway for the absorption of essential minerals," poster given at Bioavailability 88 conference, Norwich, England, August 1988.

Calcium
A Brief Introduction

Calcium in the human body is a relatively inert mineral element generally associated with bone and tooth formation. Up to 99 percent of the 850 to 1,400 gm of calcium in the adult body is found in hard tissues, that is, the bones and teeth. The term calcification, which is derived from the word calcium, is used to describe the process by which these structures acquire strength and rigidity through incorporation of calcium.

The remaining 1 percent of body calcium is widely distributed and serves in a variety of important functions. Of particular note is the function of calcium in general mineral and vitamin metabolism. Calcium serves as a catalyst in certain enzymes, triggering many other minerals and vitamins to perform their needed functions in the body. As an example, the absorption of cobalamin (vitamin B_{12}) through the intestinal wall depends on calcium.

Calcium is necessary for growth. Studies in Japan revealed that when people consume a diet deficient in calcium they are shorter. Calcium is also an important component of the blood and aids in several steps of the clotting process. Nerve and muscle response, mental alertness, pH regulation, and proper heart actions are also affected to one degree or another by the amount of calcium in the body.

Symptoms of a calcium deficiency may include stunted growth; poor quality and formation of bones and teeth;

tetany; leg cramps; slow blood clotting; excessive, lengthy, and painful menstruation; nervousness, irritability or insomnia; heart palpitations; and numbness in the extremities.

Calcium is rather poorly absorbed, with possibly only 30 percent or less of the ingested nonchelated calcium actually being taken up by the body. The factors which favorably influence ionic calcium absorption are acid in stomach (low pH), adequate amounts of vitamin D and C, adequate dietary protein, lactose, a calcium to phosphorus ratio of 1:1 to 1:2, and, ultimately, the need for calcium. Absorption takes place primarily in the duodenum. Because the duodenum is only from 10 to 12 inches in length, time plays an important role in the quantity of calcium absorbed.

Factors which depress ionic calcium absorption include oxalic acid from some vegetables, phytic acid from cereal husks, emotional instability, competing minerals, lack of dietary protein, lack of exercise, and increased intestinal motility.

The National Research Council has recommended that infants receive 360 to 540 mg daily, children 800 mg daily, teenage males and females 1,200 mg daily, and adult males and females 800 mg daily. During pregnancy and lactation an extra 400 mg of calcium should be consumed daily. These recommendations are of a general nature and do not take into consideration the bioavailability of calcium. Some forms are poorly absorbed and may result in calcium deficiencies even though adequate calcium is being ingested.

The importance of calcium to our bodies for good health and well-being cannot be overstated.

7

Calcium
When Enough Is Not Enough

I was spending a quiet evening visiting the home of my parents when I posed a question to my mother.

"What is it," I questioned, "that the body can have enough of and still be deficient in?"

"Since when did you start speaking in riddles?" chided my mother, putting down her book.

"I'm just trying to get your reaction to some ideas I'm putting together for my lecture series at a nutritional seminar next month. I've been reviewing an interesting case study of a man who was diagnosed by his doctor as suffering from symptoms of calcium deficiency. The doctor had been thorough in his examination of the patient but was puzzled because the patient's diet was not what the doctor had expected based on the test results."

"What was the nature of the patient's diet?" asked my mother.

"For one thing," I responded, "he said that he was drinking close to a gallon of milk each day, along with a normal amount of other dairy foods. Obviously, the patient was consuming more than enough calcium-containing foods, and yet, clinical tests indicated that this man suffered from calcium deficiency."

"Did you offer your doctor friend any suggestions as to the reasons for such a discrepancy between the intake and the availability of the calcium in the patient's system?" inquired my mother.

"As a matter of fact," I responded, "I told the doctor that I suspected he might find the lost calcium in the feces of the pa-

67

tient. I wasn't too surprised, then, when the doctor had a fecal sample analyzed and found an unusually high concentration of calcium. As I had suspected, even though the man was drinking about a gallon of milk a day, the calcium was not being absorbed into his system."

"Why do you suppose his absorption level was so low?" asked my mother.

"There are several factors which could contribute to low absorption of calcium," I answered. "As I explained to the doctor, unless the calcium has been properly chelated with amino acids prior to ingestion, it must be solubilized in the stomach and remain in this soluble state as it enters the intestines. Professor Helen Guthrie has written that calcium is more soluble in an acid environment and consequently is more readily absorbed from the upper portion of the intestine which tends to be acidic than from the alkaline environment in the lower portion of the intestine. Those who have more stomach acid and are not consuming antacids have a better chance of absorbing more calcium.

"As long as it remains soluble, the calcium can be chelated with a calcium-binding protein molecule found in the membrane of the cells forming the intestine. Once absorbed into the cell, the calcium must be transported across the cell by another protein molecule, which is dependent on vitamin D for its production. This is where vitamin D plays a role in calcium absorption. After being absorbed into the blood, dietary vitamin D is carried to the liver by a carrier protein called globulin. In the liver it is changed into a more active form. At this point, the new compound is transported to the kidneys by the same globulin carrier protein. In the kidneys, vitamin D is changed again to the metabolically active hormone that is essential for both the production of the calcium-binding protein in the intestinal cells and the formation of an enzyme, alkaline phosphatase. This enzyme is involved in transporting the calcium through the intestinal lining after it has been chelated with the carrier protein. Once it has been carried through the intestinal lining, the calcium can finally be absorbed and become useful to the body."

"I suppose all this means that if a person suffers from a vitamin D deficiency, then dietary calcium absorption will probably decrease," observed my mother.

"That's right," I agreed. "Provided, of course, that an amino acid chelated calcium which had been properly made was not ingested. Vitamin D does not appear to be necessary for absorption of correctly chelated calcium because the movement of the calcium amino acid chelate across the intestinal cell to the blood is not dependent upon a calcium binding protein. In other types of calcium, however, vitamin D can be a major factor in absorption because, as I said earlier, this vitamin is needed for production of the calcium-binding protein. Nevertheless, this particular patient we have been discussing gave no indications of a lack of vitamin D, so the doctor was forced to search for other solutions to the problem."

"What else can cause calcium deficiency?" prodded my mother.

"Although the solubility of a calcium ion is much greater in an alkaline medium than iron, zinc, and some other minerals, an alkaline pH in the intestine can still hinder calcium absorption," I commented. "The alkaline pH of the intestine can contribute to the formation of insoluble forms of calcium. Remember that calcium salts must first be soluble before the inorganic calcium can be chelated in the intestines and absorbed. As a person grows older, the pH of the stomach and intestines generally becomes less acid and more alkaline. Since we need an acid pH in the upper intestine, or duodenum, to maximize dietary absorption of most minerals, including calcium, a high alkaline condition can contribute to reduced calcium absorption. Antacids, even calcium-rich ones, tend to lower calcium absorption."

"Are there other factors that contribute to older people having poorer calcium absorption?" asked my mother, noticeably more interested in the direction the conversation was taking.

"When a person eats large amounts of fiber or takes laxatives, which induce diarrhea or hypermotility of the intestine," I observed, "calcium absorption is reduced. Increased consumption of fiber and the use of laxatives is a dietary characteristic of older people.

"The formation of insoluble calcium compounds in the stomach and intestines will obviously reduce calcium absorption. These insoluble compounds can be formed when we eat cereal products such as whole wheat bread which contain phytic acid or when we eat certain leafy vegetables such as spinach which contain oxalic acid. Insoluble calcium can also form in the stomach as a result of too much fat in the diet. Fatty acids form insoluble calcium soaps in the intestine that tie up the calcium.

"Finally, if there is an excessive amount of magnesium, aluminum, or phosphate or sulfur from certain amino acids in the diet, calcium absorption is reduced because these minerals interfere with the binding of calcium to the intestinal cell membrane. Further, some of them can form an insoluble precipitate with the calcium and then neither mineral can be absorbed."

"I see no practical way to avoid ingesting any of these minerals except perhaps aluminum," my mother stated. "I suppose the key here is the ratio of these minerals, to the calcium ingested."

"That's a good point," I replied. "For example, a ratio of equal amounts of calcium to phosphorus will usually maximize calcium absorption from inorganic sources."

"That would make milk an ideal source of calcium," added my mother. "It has a calcium-to-phosphorus ratio of almost one to one."

"Yes," I agreed. "According to studies conducted by George Briggs and Doris Calloway of the University of California at Berkeley, milk and hard cheese, most dark-green, leafy vegetables, and soft-boned fish are among the best food sources of calcium. These are followed by the softer cheeses, ice cream, broccoli, beans and other dried legumes, and dried figs. A fair source of calcium is cottage cheese, light cream, oranges, dates, salad greens, nuts, lima beans, parsnips, or eggs. The poorest sources of dietary calcium include almost all other foods, with red meats, for example, containing only about 3 percent calcium.

"Based on the calcium content of the average American diet, it is estimated that at least 10 percent of Americans are only getting half of the recommended calcium intake. Up to 40 percent of the males are ingesting less than two-thirds of the needed calcium, while 50 percent of the adolescent girls and 75 percent of the women fall into this category. I personally suspect that this trend is worsening because Americans are consuming larger quantities of soft drinks. Phosphoric acid is a major ingredient in many of these drinks and, when taken in excess, the phosphates, of course, interfere with calcium uptake."

"Which brings us back to the case of the calcium deficient patient who was the object of this discussion in the first place," reminded my mother. "With all the milk he was drinking, he certainly didn't fit into the category of one having a dietary deficiency.

"The doctor had already ruled out inadequate consumption of calcium," I replied, "so he concentrated on the idea of balance between minerals. These tests showed no abnormalities in the balance between calcium and the other minerals, such as magnesium and phosphorus. The patient was not taking aluminum-containing antacids. In fact, the man had never, to his recollection, experienced acid indigestion, and that became the key to his problem. After ruling out everything else, the doctor finally looked at the pH of the stomach. There he found his answer. The patient was not producing enough stomach acid to enable the calcium in the milk to be broken down and absorbed. The stomach was nearly alkaline, and the upper intestine was too alkaline."

"What was done to improve the patient's condition?" my mother questioned.

"The doctor took steps to correct the abnormally high pH

condition in the stomach," I replied. "However, he asked me about the possibility of calcium supplements to replace some of the excess milk. I reminded the doctor that if the calcium in the supplement was not chelated with amino acids or if it was improperly chelated, the calcium absorption would only be as good as it had been before. Keep in mind that if the body has to make any changes in the calcium, regardless of whether it came from food or from a dietary supplement, that calcium is subjected to all the absorption problems we discussed previously. His patient did not have adequate stomach acid to assist in changing the calcium to the form acceptable to the body. Only a properly chelated calcium supplement can successfully overcome these kinds of problems."

"How does a true calcium chelate respond to these absorption problems?" questioned my mother.

"The calcium amino acid chelate does not have to go through the normal calcium absorption pathway in the intestine, which is vitamin-D dependent," I explained. "It is absorbed by active transport as a small protein molecule (a dipeptide like molecule), provided the chelate molecule is small enough to be absorbed. This is logical if you realize that intestinal cell absorption of a true amino acid chelate happens only when the chelate is small enough to slip through the membrane of the intestinal cells as digested protein. If it isn't, then the molecule must be broken down, that is, further digested, which then possibly frees the calcium and subjects it to the vitamin D dependent mechanism."

"Was the doctor able to help the patient overcome his calcium deficiency?" asked my mother, pushing for a conclusion to the story.

"The chelated calcium that I recommended he use had an immediate effect on the patient, and the doctor continued to work with him on correcting the alkaline condition in his digestive system. However, the doctor has begun recommending a wider variety of amino acid chelated minerals to more of his patients after observing the success of this calcium supplement, so I feel like I was able to make a contribution to the improved nutrition of more than just one of his patients."

"I'm glad that you were able to make a positive contribution, and I'm certainly proud of you," said my mother. "Now just let me get back to my reading."

ADDITIONAL READING

Guthrie, H., *Introductory Nutrition* (St. Louis: Times Mirror/ Mosby College Publishing), 1986.

Kenny, A., *Intestinal Calcium Absorption and Its Regulation* (Boca Raton: C.R.C. Press), 1981.

Norman, A., *et al.*, "Basic studies on the mechanism of action of vitamin D," *Am. J. Clin. Nutr.*, 22:396, 1969.

Ebel, J., *et al.*, "Vitamin D-induced calcium-binding protein of intestinal mucosa. Relation to vitamin D dose level and long period," *Am. Clin. Nutr.*, 22:431, 1969.

Ashmead, H. D., *Intestinal Absorption of Metal Ions and Chelates* (Springfield: Charles C Thomas), 1985.

Briggs, G. and Calloway, D., *Nutrition and Physical Fitness* (Philadelphia: W. B. Saunders), 1979.

Naito, H., "Bioavailability of calcium affected by luminal and mucosal factors in the small intestine," poster presented at Bioavailability 88 conference, Norwich, England, August 1988.

Norman, A., *et al.*, eds., *Calcium-Binding Proteins in Health and Disease* (San Diego: Academic Press, Inc.), 1987.

Bronner, F. and Peterlik, M., eds., *Calcium and Phosphate Transport across Biomembranes* (New York: Academic Press), 1981.

Kies, C., ed., *Nutritional Bioavailability of Calcium* (Washington, D.C.: American Chemical Society), 1985.

8

The Roles of Calcium and Other Mineral Nutrition in Arthritis

D r. Ashmead," I heard a voice say as I made my way down the aisle of the airplane, "going my way?"

"Well, Harold, what brings you into the skies this time?" I asked, throwing my coat into the compartment above the empty seat next to my friend.

"Oh, just more business," responded my friend. "Are you headed home?"

"Yes," I said, sitting down next to him. "I've been attending a conference on health and nutrition to keep up on the latest research on mineral nutrition. How has life been treating you, Harold?"

"My life would certainly be more pleasant if it weren't for this nagging arthritis," Harold answered, buckling his seat belt.

"What have you been doing for your arthritis?" I asked sympathetically. "What can I do, other than take medication to reduce the pain?" he grumbled.

"At the conference I just attended, we discussed a number of nutritional consideration which may help improve certain arthritic conditions," I answered as the plane began its takeoff.

"Well, don't keep me in suspense," Harold said in a somewhat serious tone. "You don't realize how much discomfort and downright pain is associated with arthritis until you experience it yourself."

"At the convention, we were told of research which has

shown that magnesium, manganese, zinc, vitamins A, B_{12}, C, E, and pantothenic acid are often of nutritional value in arthritic patients."

"What effect do these nutrients have on arthritis?" my friend asked.

"Science doesn't have all the answers," I explained, "but it does have a partial picture. Dr. Mildred Seelig and some of her research colleagues have reported that abnormal magnesium metabolism, which could result from a dietary deficiency or an inability to utilize the form of magnesium ingested, can give rise to calcium deposits, which in turn lead to bone formation abnormalities. Their research has shown that some of these calcium depositions are responsive to magnesium supplements, especially magnesium that has been chelated to amino acids in such a way as to stabilize the chelate through a patented buffering process.

"Dr. Seelig's experience calls to mind a research project I was conducting with a veterinarian. The doctor had determined that a horse he was treating had developed calcium growths in some of its leg joints similar to what is seen in some forms of human arthritis. Rather than resort to surgery, the veterinarian elected to give the horse reasonably high doses of magnesium amino acid chelates. Over a period of time the calcium deposits decreased in size as confirmed by X rays, and the horse became more mobile. Dr. Seelig reported that magnesium is necessary to activate certain enzymes which inhibit the calcium depositions on the skeleton. These same enzymes can also solubilize the calcium depositions. She further related to me that most people who develop this type of problem are magnesium deficient, which supports the veterinarian's analysis of the horse's X rays.

"In analyzing certain types of arthritis, we should also pay particular attention to the composition of the synovial fluid, a sticky, viscid material that acts as a lubricant in the joints. A condition known as dry joint can occur when this synovial fluid is lacking in the joint, causing the cartilage surrounding the bone to be worn away."

"I didn't realize that synovial fluid was so important to the joints," commented my friend.

"The main component of synovial fluid is a substance called mucin, which contains hyaluronic acid," I continued as we broke through a cloud bank and squinted at the sunshine streaming through the small window. "I find it interesting that in the *Journal of Biological Chemistry* Dr. Markovitz reported that hyaluronic acid cannot be manufactured by the body without an adequate supply of magnesium, manganese, or cobalt. The latter, as you probably know, is known as vitamin B_{12} in its chelated state.

"Does this mean that people who are afflicted with arthritis have a deficiency of these minerals?" asked my friend.

"Because there are many forms of arthritis, I can't draw a general conclusion," I answered. "Nevertheless, Dr. Seelig has suggested that a magnesium deficiency is quite common among arthritic patients. Such a magnesium deficiency may result in the symptoms we just discussed.

"In the case of manganese research done at Albion Laboratories, the body mineral levels of forty-four arthritic patients were compared to healthy people. This study revealed that, as an aggregate and not as individuals, there was almost six times less manganese than normal in the bodies of those people whom their physicians had diagnosed as being arthritics."

"Are you saying that if I didn't have enough manganese in my body to manufacture sufficient quantities of hyaluronic acid for the synovial fluid, that my joints would not be properly lubricated and could become stiff and painful to move?" concluded my friend.

"That could well be a contributing factor to certain types of arthritic conditions," I agreed. "Unfortunately, arthritis is usually more complicated than a simple mineral deficiency. For example, other researchers have discovered that the blood levels of vitamin A and the B-complex vitamins are generally lower in many arthritic patients than in healthy persons. The same comparison holds true of vitamins E and D. At present we don't know the functions of these vitamins in those types of arthritis except vitamin E. Research has shown that when sufficient quantities of vitamin E are present in the body, it inhibits the production of hyaluronidase."

"What is hyaluronidase?" interrupted my friend.

"Hyaluronidase is an enzyme that has the capacity to break down the hyaluronic acid (a mucopolysaccharide which binds protein, water, and other substances together to form the synovial fluid) in the synovial fluid of the joints," I explained. "It has been demonstrated in a study by C. Regan and A. DeLamader that when hyaluronidase is injected into the joints of animals, the hyaluronic acid which is normally produced is destroyed, resulting in decreased viscosity of the synovial fluids in the joints. The mobility of the animals was significantly reduced and they exhibited many other characteristics of an arthritic condition.

"That same study also revealed that hyaluronidase has a tendency to destroy the synovial fluid in the joints, and to spread this decomposed fluid to the lymphatic vessels, where it is absorbed in excessive amounts, causing swelling of the joints."

"You mentioned that vitamin E was found to interfere with the production of this destructive enzyme," my friend commented. "Is there anything else that will prevent hyaluronidase from being manufactured in the body?"

"I don't know of anything," I answered, "but perhaps certain minerals may help. For example, as early as 1969, some of the scientists at Albion Laboratories participated in a research project involving turkeys which researchers at Utah State University had diagnosed as being afflicted with synovitis syndrome."

"What's that?"

"Synovitis is a condition characterized by leg weakness and a swelling of the leg joints, focusing on the synovial sheaths of the joints. Professor William Hoekstra identified these joint and bone deformities in poultry as being similar to rheumatoid arthritis in humans. At any rate, the turkeys diagnosed as having synovitis were given magnesium, calcium, zinc, iron, manganese, copper, and cobalt as amino acid chelates. Over a period of two weeks, most of the swelling in the joints of the turkeys went down, and those birds that had not been able to walk regained their mobility. Upon final analysis, it was determined that the mineral composition of the synovial fluid in the afflicted birds was modified, presumably because of the change in the mineral nutrition of the turkeys. The minerals fed to the turkeys apparently had a negative effect on the production of the enzyme hyaluronidase, resulting in a beneficial effect on the maintenance of the synovial fluid."

"Which mineral do you think had the most beneficial effect?" he asked.

"I don't know for sure," I responded, "but calcium would be high on my list."

"Why calcium?" he wanted to know. "I thought calcium was one of the causes of arthritis."

"Only when it is not metabolized properly, and the magnesium in the diet would have helped in calcium metabolism. You see, calcium blocks lead metabolism."

"Why is lead a factor in arthritis?" my friend asked.

"According to a study by C. Blackburn published in the *Journal of Biological Chemistry*, even if the hyaluronidase enzyme is produced, it can't destroy the synovial fluid unless there is enough lead in the body to activate that enzyme and start it on its destructive course. According to an Albion Laboratories study on mineral levels in the body, arthritic patients show approximately 38 percent higher levels of lead in their bodies than do healthy persons."

"What you are saying is that this research has shown that most people who have arthritis don't have sufficient amounts of vitamin E in their bodies to prevent the production of hyaluronidase. At the same time, because these people have improper calcium metabolism due to a magnesium deficiency, along with higher than normal amounts of lead in their bodies, the lead may activate the enzyme, resulting in destruction of the lubricating fluids in the joints, which in turn results in swelling. The improperly metabolized calcium is deposited on the joints because of a magnesium deficiency, and finally, since there isn't enough manganese in the body to produce enough synovial fluid to keep up with its destruction by the hyaluronidase, the joints become stiff and swollen, and I end up with arthritis!"

As the plane broke out of the cloud cover and the broad expanse of the Great Plains opened to view, my friend asked me what might be done to stop the hyaluronidase enzyme from destroying the fluids in his joints.

"If I had arthritis," I told him, "I would probably want to discuss with my physician a good nutritional program, which would include plenty of vitamins, particularly A, B-complex, C, and E. I would also want to supplement my diet with manganese, zinc, calcium, and magnesium, provided these minerals had been properly chelated with amino acids."

"Why would you supplement with those specific minerals?" Harold asked.

"We have already talked about the importance of manganese," I reminded him. "It is essential to the body's manufacture of hyaluronic acid used in the lubricating fluids of the joints. These fluids also require magnesium and cobalt from vitamin B_{12}. According to A. Markovitz and his research colleague, a deficiency of any one of these nutrients will cause a reduction in the production of synovial fluids because each one is essential to activate a specific enzyme that participates in the synthesis of hyaluronic acid.

"But magnesium has another possible role that is equally important," I continued. "Research suggests that if the body contains adequate amounts of magnesium which is not inactivated by calcium, it, like the calcium, may prevent the lead from activating the destructive enzymes, even when there are higher than normal levels of lead in the body. If we look at magnesium in that light, it plays a significant role in preserving the synovial fluids besides helping in the metabolism of calcium. In fact, two physicians doing research in Florida told me that when they supplemented their patients' diets with properly chelated magnesium, they observed an increase in the amount of lead being excreted by their patients.

"When in proper balance, calcium is 8.2 times more prevalent in the body than magnesium. In the arthritic patient, this ratio increases to as much as 9.9 to 1 in favor of calcium. Under the latter condition, the calcium interferes with the magnesium so that it cannot function adequately in the body."

"In the case of the arthritic," my friend interrupted, "the magnesium appears to be inactivated by the excess calcium so it can't stop the lead from activating the destructive hyaluronidase enzyme. As the hyaluronidase destroys the synovial fluids, there is a tendency to restrict the movement of the joint. When this occurs, an environment is created that is conducive to the deposition of the excess calcium in the joints. Coupled with the other deficiencies of vitamins and minerals as well as other factors, the possible result is arthritis."

"That's one way it could happen," I agreed. "Based on the research I've seen over the years, it seems that a large percentage of arthritis could be prevented through changes in the diet, including supplements. I'm not the only one who feels that way either. The United States government published a book on human nutrition which was based on a joint study by the University of Minnesota and the University of Nebraska. In this book, the Department of Agriculture concluded that 50 percent of Americans who suffered from arthritis could be cured or the arthritis prevented in the first place through improvements or changes in their diets. The government further concluded that the incidence of this disease was directly related to the depletion of minerals in the soil over the past few decades. As you know, the soil is our original source of minerals in the diet."

"Well," said my friend as he settled back with a magazine, "you've certainly convinced me that I ought to re-examine my own nutritional program to see if there is room for improvement. That will be the first thing on my agenda when we return home."

ADDITIONAL READING

Seelig, M., *et al.*, "Rationale for use of magnesium in treatment of calcinosis: Application to myositis ossificans progressiva," paper given at annual meeting of American College of Nutrition, Washington, DC, 1984.

Fredericks, C., *Nutrition Guide for the Prevention and Cure of Common Ailments and Disease* (New York: Simon and Schuster), 1982.

Ashmead, H., "Metabolic Systems and their Mineral Activators," paper given at a Miller Seminar for physicians, Denver, December, 1968.

Markovitz, A., *et al.*, "The Biosynthesis of Hyaluronic Acid by Group A Streptococcus," *J. Biol. Chem.*, 234:2343, 1959.

Ashmead, H.D., *et al.*, "Mineral analysis of hair as related to metabolic disorders," paper given at Southern California Academy of Nutritional Res., Los Angeles, October 1979.

Regan, C. and DeLamater, A., "Hydrolysis of hyaluronic acid of human joint fluid *in vivo*" *Proc. Soc. Exp. Biol. Med.*, 50:349, 1942.

Hinz, P., *et al.*, "Effect of feeding metalosates to staphylococcic-synovitis turkeys," paper presented to Utah Feed Manufacturers Assoc., Logan, 1969.

Blackburn, C., "The role of lead in the reduction of the erythrocyte sedimentation rate by hyaluronidase," *J. Biol. Chem.*, 178:855, 1949.

Freeman, W., *et al.*, "Magnesium and hyaluronidase inhibitor of blood serum," *Proc. Soc. Exp. Biol. Med.* 70: 524, 1949.

Weir, E., *Benefits From Human Nutritional Research, Human Nutrition Report No. 2* (Washington D.C.: U.S. Department of Agriculture), 1971.

Nancollas, G., ed, *Biological Mineralization and Demineralization* (Berlin: Springer-Verlag), 1982.

Chromium
A Brief Introduction

A lthough the functions of chromium are not well understood, it is the feeling of many nutritionists that this trace mineral will soon be recognized as one of the most important elements in nutritional supplementation. It is considered an essential nutrient in human nutrition. Because chromium is lost through many of the refining processes that our modern food undergoes, there is an increasing need to identify its functions more clearly.

Chromium is poorly absorbed from the intestines. It is estimated that between 0.5 percent and 3.0 percent of an oral dose of trivalent chromium is absorbed. The rest is excreted in the feces. When divalent chromium is ingested it will immediately precipitate in the alkaline pH of the intestines and not be absorbed at all. If the chromium is properly chelated to amino acids, that is, organically bound, its absorption is considerably higher according to the National Research Council.

We know that chromium stimulates enzymes involved in glucose metabolism for energy and that it increases the effectiveness of insulin. It aids in the binding of insulin to the cell, which in turn allows glucose to be taken up by the cell.

More recent studies have shown a correlation between chromium and the synthesis of fatty acids. Studies are now under way to determine why the addition of chromium to the diet seems to reverse atherosclerosis (that it does is, more or less, scientifically established). It is my opinion that the

83

mechanism involves the metabolism of glucose, which, if improperly metabolized, is converted to fats. Fats are a major portion of the atherosclerotic plaque. If the sugar is properly metabolized, as it is in the presence of chromium, the body then has a chance to deplete the blood fat with the phospholipids and other metabolic means without a constant replenishment being furnished. A deficiency of chromium has been associated with reduced glucose tolerance and increasing incidence of diabetes. It has also been associated with hypoglycemia.

There is a steady decline in body chromium levels with advancing age. A chromium deficiency has also been related to retarded growth, problems with amino acid metabolism, decreased body reserves of glycogen, and possibly atherosclerosis through increased aortic lesions.

The National Research Council tentatively recommends daily intake of between 50 and 200 micrograms per day of chromium for adults. This is based on the assumption that only 1 to 2 percent of the ingested chromium will be absorbed.

9

The Roles of Chromium in Diabetes and Atherosclerosis

J ust recently I was visiting in my office with a young mother who was an employee of mine. She had expressed concern over the health of her family and had come to ask my advice.

"As I mentioned earlier," she began, "my husband has been diabetic since he was about fifteen years old but seems to be controlling it quite well with insulin injections. I guess my main concern is for the children, since diabetes has been linked somewhat to hereditary factors. I would like to reduce as much as possible our children's chances of becoming diabetic, and I was hoping you could help to pinpoint some nutritional factors which may be involved in the onset of this disease."

"Your concerns are understandable," I said, offering the young woman a seat. "Nutritionists have spent countless hours researching the effects of nutrition on diabetes, and, although the disease itself is still largely a mystery, several findings have proved to have some merit.

"The late Dr. Henry Schroeder did a considerable amount of research with diabetes and concluded that a chromium deficiency is frequently present with diabetes. Others have confirmed the relationship of chromium to diabetes. In fact, I have a book here written by Dr. Len Mervyn where he discusses this relationship. In a section devoted to chromium, Dr. Mervyn says:

The importance of chromium to man has only recently become apparent with the discovery of its role in allowing the muscles to take up sugar from the blood. Deficiency of the mineral leads to a condition almost indistinguishable from mild diabetes mellitus, with symptoms including a high fasting blood sugar, due to the inability of the body tissues to remove the sugar from the blood, and a high urinary glucose output. Hence, some diabetics respond favorably to chromium supplementation, which suggests that their condition is primarily due to lack of the mineral. This is particularly so in juvenile diabetes, where the diet has been shown to be low in chromium due mainly to a high consumption of refined carbohydrates coupled with low protein intake. Lack of chromium also appears to be involved in the development of maturity-onset diabetes since it has been found that levels of the mineral in the tissue drop with age. When these individuals are given extra chromium in their diet, between 40 and 66 percent of them improve and either come off insulin altogether or survive on lower doses . . .

There is little doubt that lack of chromium or the inability to utilize it is a factor in the development of diabetes. As modern refining of foods and over consumption of refined carbohydrates like sugar and starch remove the chromium naturally present, it seems a sensible move to supplement the diet with chromium, particularly for anyone suffering from diabetes.[1]

"I guess that means that I should pay more attention to the amount of chromium that my family gets," said the concerned young woman.

"That's right," I agreed, "and for more reasons than one. Adequate chromium may reduce the chance that your children will become diabetic, and since your husband has had diabetes for some time, a chromium supplement may prevent him from developing other complications common in diabetics."

"What other complications are you referring to?" she inquired.

"It has been established that a chromium deficiency is also a factor in atherosclerosis because diabetics who frequently have large amounts of fats in their blood due to faulty metabolism are prone to atherosclerosis. This doesn't mean that all diabetics have atherosclerosis," I continued. "The American

Medical Association, in commenting on the dietary goals of U.S. citizens, concluded that there is no direct relationship between the amount of fat in the diet or blood and the incidence of atherosclerosis.

"Yet atherosclerosis is characterized by a buildup of plaques in the large and medium-size arteries. These plaques are made up of cholesterol and fat, or lipid, material, and they interfere with the flow of blood. A buildup of fat deposits on the arterial walls restricting the flow of blood suggests that the body may be having a problem metabolizing that material. That's probably one of the reasons why plaques are being deposited in the first place."

"Isn't atherosclerosis common in people without diabetes?" the woman questioned.

"Yes, it is," I agreed, "but in the study of atherosclerosis, some interesting connections have been discovered. Work which was done by Dr. Henry Schroeder and his associates established that severe atherosclerosis is usually associated with abnormalities in the body's glucose metabolism. A low tolerance to glucose, the sugar in the blood, is chromium related, and it was discovered that an experimental chromium deficiency has consistently led to diabetes.

"Chromium appears to be essential for the metabolism of dietary fats and lipids as well," I continued. "If we were to look at people who had atherosclerosis, we would see that their serum cholesterol and other lipid levels were elevated. In this condition, there is less tolerance to ingested or injected glucose, and often a mild state of diabetes is fostered. Eventually, because of the inability to metabolize these fats effectively, plaques begin to grow on the arterial walls."

"But how can you be sure that these conditions are related directly to chromium?" the young lady wanted to know.

"I think that it is worth noting that scientists can duplicate these same biological and pathological changes under experimental conditions simply by introducing a chromium-deficient diet," I explained. "Dr. Schroeder did something else that incriminated chromium and tends to substantiate the connection between its deficiency state and atherosclerosis. He and his associates obtained aorta tissue samples from people all across the United States who had died from atherosclerotic heart disease. They also obtained tissues from people who had died from other forms of cardiovascular diseases. These tissues were assayed along with tissues taken from healthy individuals who had died in accidents. The researchers found that those who had died as a result of atherosclerosis had chromium levels significantly lower than those otherwise healthy people who had died in accidents. When you consider that atherosclerosis can be induced experimentally by creating a chromium deficiency, it is only logical to conclude that a definite relationship exists between chromium deficiency and atherosclerosis."

"From what you're telling me, chromium deficiencies may be a significant factor in anyone's health picture," commented the young lady. "Do you actually see it as a widespread problem?"

"According to *Benefits from Human Nutrition Research* published by the United States Department of Agriculture, the U.S. death rate in 1900 from cardiovascular disease was only 20 percent. By 1960 over half of U.S. deaths were attributable to cardiovascular disease. This observation is significant when you consider that, generally speaking, chromium levels in the tissues of people in the United States have been declining in this century," I answered.

"Government research has also discovered that those geographical areas within the United States which had the highest death rates from cardiovascular disease also had soils depleted of chromium and other nutrients. This would indicate that foods with similar deficiencies had been consumed. Dr. Schroeder also deduced from his study that if we increased the intake of chromium, we would reduce the risk of heart disease."

"I suppose that my family should consider chromium supplementation," said the young lady, "even if we do it just to reduce our chances of heart disease and atherosclerosis. I've read that most diabetics actually succumb to conditions indirectly related to diabetes."

"Don't misunderstand me," I replied. "I'm not trying to diminish the more direct relationship that chromium has to

diabetes, but merely to point out some obvious deficiency consequences. Let me read you what Dr. Helen Guthrie says
about this relationship in her book *Introductory Nutrition:*

> Low intakes of chromium have been associated with reduced
> tolerance to glucose and an increasing incidence of diabetes,
> both of which occur with increasing age. Many cases of mild
> glucose intolerance can be treated successfully with chromium.
> Studies of chromium in the body show that the fetus obtains a
> generous supply from the material organism but that in the
> United States there is a steady decline throughout life.[2]

"This would seem to indicate that chromium supplementation in children would be as good as anything to reduce their
chances of becoming diabetic," I concluded. "And your husband's condition probably wouldn't be harmed by increasing
his chromium intake, although the supplements may not
reverse his disease entirely considering how long he has had it.
He ought to look at other nutrition too, including zinc and
vitamins."

"I think you've given me the information I need to improve
our family's nutrition program," said the young woman.
"Thank you so much for your time today."

I told her she was welcome to the information and reminded her to be certain that the chromium she chose was chelated
properly to amino acids. If she and her family ingested chromium as an ionic salt or as part of a large molecule, such as
yeast, that had to be digested first, very little chromium would
be absorbed from either source.

NOTES

1. L. Mervyn, *Minerals and Your Health* (New Canaan: Keats
   Publishing, Inc., 1981), p. 94.
2. H. Guthrie, *Introductory Nutrition* (St. Louis: C.V. Mosby Co.,
   1975), p. 179.

ADDITIONAL READING

Mervyn, L., *Minerals and Your Health* (New Canaan: Keats Publishing, Inc.), 1981.

Schroeder, H., "Chromium deficiency in rats: A syndrome stimulating diabetes mellitus with retarded growth," *J. Nutr.*, 88:439, 1966.

Mertz, W. and Cornatzer, W., eds., *Newer Trace Elements in Nutrition* (New York: Marcel Dekker), 125 – 195, 1971.

Schroeder, H., *et al.*, "Abnormal trace elements in man—Chromium," *J. Chronic Diseases*, 15: 941, 1962.

Weir, E., *Benefits from Human Nutrition Research, Human Nutrition Report No. 2* (Washington, DC: U.S. Department of Agriculture), 1971.

Davies, I., *The Clinical Significance of the Essential Biological Metals* (Springfield: Charles C Thomas), 94 – 103, 1972.

Guthrie, H., *Introductory Nutrition* (St. Louis: C.V. Mosby Co.), 1975.

Mertz, W., ed., *Trace Elements in Human and Animal Nutrition* (San Diego: Academic Press, Inc.), 1987.

Cobalt
A Brief Introduction

A lthough the functions of cobalt are not well understood, because it is the central portion of vitamin B_{12}, its role in that vitamin is much clearer. Cobalt is considered to be an essential nutrient in man and appears to have several functions that are separate from its role in vitamin B_{12}.

When ingested as an inorganic cobalt salt, about 26 percent of the mineral is absorbed from the small intestine. If there is a cobalt deficiency, higher amounts may be absorbed. As part of the vitamin B_{12}, it is equally well absorbed from food as from a supplement.

No RDA has been established for cobalt in spite of its essential nature. An RDA for adults of 3 mg per day has been established for vitamin B_{12}.

Since animal products are the major food source for this mineral, vegetarians are more susceptible to a cobalt deficiency. All the function and symptoms of deficiency which pertain to iron are applicable to cobalt, in addition to problems with nerves, growth, and perhaps the thyroid gland.

10
Cobalt
The Center of Vitamin B$_{12}$

A few years ago, I had the opportunity to meet Dr. Leonard Mervyn, who lives in England and was on the research team that developed vitamin B$_{12}$. I found it fascinating to sit and talk to him about his discoveries.

He told me that vitamin B$_{12}$ was first isolated in 1948 as a pure compound. Subsequent chemical analysis revealed that the vitamin was actually cobalt-linked, or chelated to organic molecules by covalent bonds. The resulting product is chelated cobalt.

The discovery was exciting because it tied to research that had been done in the 1930s. The research determined that a cobalt deficiency existed in certain animals, primarily in sheep and cows. When cobalt was supplemented, the animals got better. "Because cows and sheep are ruminants and their stomachs are like fermentation vats, they chelated the cobalt supplements in their stomachs and converted them to vitamin B$_{12}$," Dr. Mervyn explained. Later it was shown that these animals were really not cobalt deficient but vitamin B$_{12}$ deficient. That, of course, did not occur until in the 1950s, after the isolation of vitamin B$_{12}$.

"Is there such a thing as a cobalt deficiency," I asked, "or is a deficiency manifested only as a vitamin B$_{12}$ deficiency?"

"There was a time I would have said that the only certain function of cobalt in humans is in its incorporation into the vitamin B$_{12}$ molecule," he answered. "Thus I would have con-

93

cluded that all deficiency symptoms can be cured by vitamin B_{12}. But today I am not entirely sure that is correct."

"Why is that?" I asked.

"Well," he explained, "there is some evidence that cobalt may be essential for some body functions other than those in which vitamin B_{12} is involved. You see, as researchers have analyzed the bodies of men and animals, they have found the mineral in tissues in forms other than as part of the vitamin B_{12} molecule. That would suggest to me that perhaps it has additional functions to those of vitamin B_{12}."

He continued, "It is interesting that cobalt must be complexed or chelated before it is an effective nutrient. Vitamin B_{12} is absorbed by both active and passive mechanisms. The passive mechanism is by diffusion, although absorption is less than 1 percent by that process.

"Active absorption requires that the vitamin be bound to a special protein found in the intestine near the pyloric valve and in the duodenum. The vitamin is bound to this protein called intrinsic factor and transported into the intestinal cells. If the pH of the intestines is elevated to an alkaline pH, absorption is reduced. Once absorbed into the intestinal cell, the vitamin B_{12} appears in the blood bound to specific proteins."

"That sounds very similar to the absorption mechanisms of mineral salts," I mused.

"It probably is," he agreed. "The late professor Eric Underwood, who discovered the need for cobalt, has written that the absorption of a cobalt salt from the intestines uses the same pathway as iron. In fact, there is competition between iron and cobalt at the intestinal absorption sites for carrier proteins to chelate them for uptake."

"Then," I concluded, "cobalt would probably be absorbed better if it were chelated in the laboratory prior to ingestion."

Smiling at me, Dr. Mervyn said, "I know that your work has been in the area of chelation and I think you are probably right in your assessment of cobalt. But for practical purposes, I see no reason to supplement cobalt when we have vitamin B_{12} available instead. It will do the same job as cobalt."

I disagreed with him on the basis of his description of the intestinal environment necessary for absorption of either vitamin B_{12} or cobalt. Each requires that the intestine be highly acid. In my work with chelated minerals, I had discovered that if a mineral is chelated correctly with amino acids, its absorption is not affected by the pH of the stomach or intestines. It will have been buffered in such a way that it no longer reacts to changes in the pH. And because in a stable amino acid chelate the metal is part of a very small protein molecule of just two amino acids, it will be absorbed into the body at the protein absorption sites in the intestine. Since the mineral is completely unreactive in this chelated form, in reality, it is smuggled into the body as part of the protein molecule rather than as a metal. That's why when minerals are properly chelated, their absorption is high even though toxicity is so low as to be almost nonexistent.

I then asked Dr. Mervyn what would happen if a person suffered from a cobalt deficiency.

"Vitamin B_{12} deficiency is much easier to describe," he said. "It is involved in the production of red blood cells. Some forms of anemia respond to vitamin B_{12} treatment better than to iron. It may be involved in the nervous system. The myelin sheath, which coats nerves, deteriorates when there is a vitamin B_{12} deficiency. There are several enzymes that are also responsive to vitamin B_{12}. These include methylamonyl-CoA mutase, methyl tetrahydrofolate oxide reductase, homocysteine methyltransferase, and ribonucleotide reductase. In a deficiency state, propionate and methionine metabolism are interrupted, and there is a failure of deoxyribonucleic acid to be synthesized.

"The cobalt ion is believed to activate several enzymes independent of vitamin B_{12}, but only glycol glycine lipeptidase has been identified. According to some Russian researchers, cobalt has been found to enhance the immune response in animals. Oral cobalt supplementation has been reported to reduce the incidence of atherosclerosis in humans. And finally, cobalt has been reported to be necessary for the synthesis of the thyroid hormone. Investigators in the Soviet Union have noticed that in areas where there are cobalt deficiencies in the

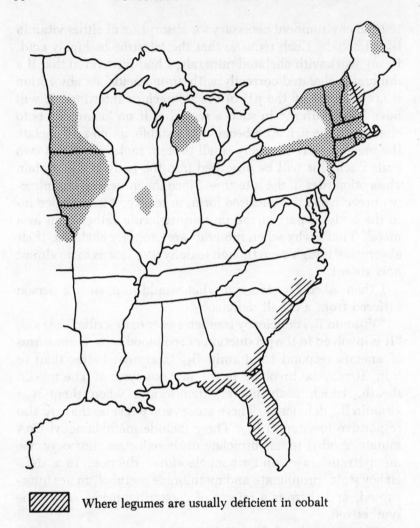

Where legumes are usually deficient in cobalt

Where legumes may be marginally deficient in cobalt

Figure 10 – 1. **Areas in the United States where legumes contain low levels of cobalt.** SOURCE: W. Allaway, *The Effect of Soils and Fertilizers on Human and Animal Nutrition* (Washington, DC: US Department of Agriculture, 1975), p. 14.

soil and also in the foods of people living in these areas, there is a much higher incidence of goiter in the people and their animals.

As he told me this, I thought about a map I had seen in a booklet entitled *The Effect of Soils and Fertilizers on Human and Animal Nutrition* published by the U.S. government. This map showed several areas in the United States that were cobalt deficient. It included New England, parts of the Midwest, and the South Atlantic (Figure 10-1). I wondered whether we may have a problem in the United States. Although I didn't know the answer as far as a deficiency in humans is concerned, I recognized that more of us are supplementing our diets with vitamin B_{12} or amino acid chelated cobalt and that suggested to me that there may be a need.

At this point in our conversation, the subject changed and we moved to another topic.

ADDITIONAL READING

Mervyn, L., "The metabolism of the cobalamins" in Florkin, M. and Stotz, E., eds., *Comprehensive Biochemistry* (Amsterdam: Elsevier Publishing Co.), V. 21, 153–178, 1971.

Allaway, W., *The Effect of Soils and Fertilizers on Human and Animal Nutrition* (Washington, DC: U.S. Department of Agriculture), 1975.

Underwood, E., *Trace Elements in Human and Animal Nutrition* (New York: Academic Press), 132–158, 1977.

Davies, I., *The Clinical Significance of the Essential Biological Metals* (Springfield: Charles C Thomas), 94–102, 1972.

Underwood, E., "Cobalt" in Hegsted, D., *et al.*, eds, *Present Knowledge in Nutrition* (Washington, DC: The Nutrition Foundation), 317–324, 1976.

Mervyn, L., *Minerals and Your Health* (New Canaan: Keats Publishing, Inc.), 1981.

Copper
A Brief Introduction

C opper was recognized as a trace element or micronutrient in the human body as early as 1928 as a result of its value in connection with iron in preventing anemia. Copper works to absorb and carry oxygen as a component of hemoglobin and also facilitates the absorption of iron into the bloodstream.

Copper has more recently been identified as an element essential to increasing resistance to stress and disease. In addition, protein metabolism and general body healing processes have been linked to copper. In fact, copper plays a vital role in the health and proper functioning of each and every body cell.

With the small amount of copper actually present in the body, it is understandable that its importance as a mineral nutrient has been overlooked. However, as biochemical analysis of cellular functions becomes more sophisticated, the need for adequate copper levels in the body has become increasingly apparent.

A deficiency of copper can result in general weakness and anemia, reduced immune response, impaired respiration, skin sores, brittle nails, and sometimes constipation.

Although copper has been recognized as an essential trace element for human nutrition, no RDA has been established for this element by the National Research Council. Nevertheless the N.R.C. has recommended that between 2 and 3 milligrams per day be ingested. An occasional intake of up to 10 milligrams per day is considered safe.

11

Copper
Little Things Mean a Lot

A s I surveyed the shelves of a local nutritional food store, I caught the eye of a lady who seemed puzzled by the label on a bottle of mineral supplements.

"Why do you suppose the manufacturer includes such a small amount of copper with the rest of these minerals?" she questioned, half to herself. "If it's that insignificant, why include it at all?"

Recognizing an opportunity to share some information on mineral nutrition, I offered an explanation. "If we look at the amount of copper in our bodies in comparison to other nutrients, we wouldn't think it was important. In fact, copper constitutes only 0.00015 percent of body weight, which means that there are between 80 and 100 milligrams of copper in the average human body; that's approximately one-third of an aspirin tablet. Of that amount, about half is in the bones and muscles and the remainder is distributed throughout the blood and other tissues of the body. It exists in the blood chelated to albumin or to amino acids, according to Professor Helen Guthrie.

"Because there is such a small amount of copper in our bodies to meet our needs, it doesn't take much of something else to remove it from its functioning areas. When that small amount of copper is displaced or deficient in our diets, our bodies can get into trouble quickly. For example, in a study of 1,700 experimental animals, Dr. Robert Coffey found that immunity to disease was related to body levels of copper. Those

101

animals that were sick and could not develop an immune response had lower than normal copper levels in the blood. Dr. Coffey indicated that by increasing dietary copper levels, their resistance to infections could be enhanced. He used a special copper amino acid chelate supplied by Albion Laboratories, which other university research had shown was absorbed in higher quantities."

"What other kinds of trouble can a lack of copper cause in the body?" questioned the lady.

"Chelated copper," I responded, "is involved in activating many of the protein building enzymes which build or repair body tissues. That small amount of copper is involved in such important chemical reactions within the body as iron absorption, energy release within the cells, pigmentation of the hair and skin, formation of protective myelin coating for nerve fibers, and synthesis of elastin. In this latter function, as part of the enzyme monoamine oxidase, present in elastin and connective tissues, copper assists in oxidative dissemination of lysine in peptide chains to aminadipic semialdehyde, which forms the cross linkages of our vascular tissues. Simply stated, a copper deficiency could result in less elasticity in those tissues and lead to spontaneous ruptures or aneurysms of the arteries and the aorta of the heart, as well as producing a fragile skeleton.

"Copper's added importance to elastin formation in developing tendons is shown in studies by Susan Hildebran and Dr. John Hunt, which were published in a medical journal. They reported that a specific type of amino acid chelated copper manufactured by Albion Laboratories, when included as a dietary supplement, aided in normal tendon development in copper-deficient animals. The rates of tendon development were determined by X rays. Since tendons are basically composed of collagen and elastin, which require copper for their formation, when a copper deficiency exists, the growing animal, like human beings, experiences lameness and general stiffness."

"That's probably more than I wanted to know about copper," chuckled my new acquaintance, "but I am interested in copper as it relates to tissue repair. A while back I was told by my doctor that a deficiency of copper can become a factor in the development of stomach ulcers."

"That is very possible," I replied, sorting through the shelves of vitamin and mineral supplements. "Since most of the body tissues, including the stomach, are made up of protein, copper's role in that protein metabolism becomes extremely important."

"How does the copper actually affect the protein metabolism in the body?" asked the lady, putting a bottle of copper supplement in her shopping basket.

"When foods containing protein reach the stomach," I answered, "they begin to be broken down or digested into amino acids, the building blocks of protein. This process continues in the intestines. Once the digestive fluids composed of acids and enzymes have broken the food protein down to amino acids, these amino acids are absorbed through specific sites in the intestine into the blood. From there the amino acids are moved to the various areas of the body where they are reassembled into new types of protein to be used in muscles, organs, skin, hair, etc. It is at this point that copper becomes indispensable. As I said earlier, copper is necessary to activate lysyl oxidase for the manufacture of connective tissue, which holds the protein together to form the various tissues and organs, including the stomach. Further, as I also said earlier, copper is essential in making elastin, which allows the muscles and other tissues and organs to be flexible. The synthesis of mature elastin and collagen is controlled by the availability of copper. When there is a deficiency, structural changes occur in the tissues because the protein molecules are not held together properly, and they become less elastic."

"That's what happened to the animals that had the tendon problems," the lady concluded. "With so much dependence on copper by the body, doesn't the small amount that's in the body get spread pretty thin at times?"

"When we take away even a small amount of copper at a local site for use in another area, we do face the possibility of depletion in a particular organ," I responded. "Keep in mind that a total absence of body copper would result in death. However, what we are concerned with is less than optimal body levels of copper. When a deficiency occurs, the physiological response is negative. We saw that negative response in the growing animals with tendon problems and the experimental animals that couldn't properly develop their immune systems. A similar kind of negative response to a copper deficiency may be a factor in some instances of stomach ulcers, and that is presumably what your doctor had in mind when he made his comment on the relationship between copper deficiencies and ulcers. In some instances, however, the site deficiency is caused by an external factor rather than a dietary deficiency. For example, we frequently take aspirin for pain. That pain is often the result of inflammation. The aspirin, besides masking pain, also tends to reduce that inflammation, and this is where copper comes in.

"Dr. John Sorenson reported in a medical journal that when we swallow large amounts of aspirin for pain, that ingested aspirin, through the process of synthetic chelation, combines with the copper in the tissues of the stomach to form a copper salicylate. It then carries that sequestered copper to the site of the pain, where this additional transported copper plays a key role in helping the aspirin reduce inflammation. At that point, we experience a relief from the pain. Dr. F.R. Mangan of England has observed that certain copper chelates produce profound anti-inflammatory responses in laboratory animals and presumably human beings."

"What does that have to do with ulcers?" questioned the lady.

"Inflammation is closely related to ulcers, theoretically," I went on. "One 5-grain aspirin tablet can tie up three times as much copper as our entire body contains. If the aspirin reduces inflammation by combining with copper and then carrying the copper to the inflamed area, a person should be concerned with high aspirin intake. The aspirin contains no copper when it is swallowed, so it has to get it from somewhere. If the aspirin is able to tie up the copper from the stomach lining and then remove it to another area of the body, it can cause a local depletion of copper in the stomach tissue. This deficiency allows inflammation to begin in the stomach, and under these conditions an ulcer can eventually erupt. If left unattended, and if the ulcer commences bleeding, massive doses of aspirin could prevent the blood oozing from the sore from clotting. This circumstance, according to Dr. Mark Everett, would aggravate the ulcerous condition."

"I have always thought of an ulcer as an open sore," remarked the lady. "Does it usually begin with a minor inflammation of the stomach wall?"

"Keep in mind that there are many types of ulcers," I explained. "As a general description, the ulcer results in the loss of the mucus on the surface of the stomach cells, thus causing a gradual disintegration of the tissues forming the stomach. Inflammation is part of the ulceration process. Generally, we think of inflammation as being pain associated with redness and color. It is actually the reaction to injury, which in this case is the ulcer. That is probably part of what people feel when they have an ulcer. The inflammation accompanying the ulcer is marked by discharges of the mucus lining of the stomach and further breakdown of the connective tissues and fibrin which the copper originally helped put together. So the inflammation we are seeing in the stomach ulcer may actually be the breakdown of the stomach wall, which may be due in part to a local or general body deficiency of copper. If the copper were present, it would help arrest the inflammation and regenerate new stomach tissue. When copper is depleted through artificial means such as massive doses of aspirin or as a result of a general body deficiency, the stomach tissues begin to break down. Inflammation accompanies this breakdown, and we may feel it as a stomach ulcer. While I don't dispute current medical treatments for stomach ulcers, it seems to me that physicians would be well advised to include copper supplements as part of their recovery programs."

I continued, "Part of my conclusion is based on research done by Dr. Sorenson at the University of Cincinnati Medical Center. He reported that copper appears to be closely linked to the natural prevention of inflammation in the body. In laboratory rats, where ulcers had been induced, Dr. Sorenson could bring about rapid healing when he fed the animals a copper chelate.

The level of stomach acids, which tend to eat at the stomach wall, and the quantity of gastric pepsin, were reduced by the addition of the copper chelate. Pepsin is an enzyme that functions in gastric acids to break down protein into small groups of amino acids. If the mucus which coats the stomach is removed for some reason, such as a copper deficiency, then the protein which makes up the stomach wall can be digested through a breakdown of the peptide linkages, especially in cases where a copper deficiency exists. Keep in mind that copper is required to put some of those linkages together in the first place. This digestion process occurs more rapidly when there is a copper deficiency, which further points out the necessity of adequate amounts of copper."

"Then too little copper in the body could contribute to stomach ulcers," the lady concluded.

"It appears that is correct," I agreed. "During a research project in which I was assisted by several doctors, we found that people who suffered from stomach ulcers averaged almost 23 percent less copper in their bodies as compared to nonulcerous subjects.

"Further," I continued, "Dr. Samuel Townsend demonstrated in laboratory animals a much faster healing process in surgically induced ulcers when the animals received a copper chelate. Five days after ulcer induction, the animals receiving the chelated copper were in a state of repair. The animals receiving the chelates tended to remain at least five days ahead of the other group throughout the experiment."

Not only is the healing process accelerated in the presence of copper supplements, but inflammation is also controlled when copper chelates are administered orally, according to research published by Professors Peter May and David Williams of the University of Wales. They reported that rheumatoid arthritis, which generally manifests itself as inflammation of the fibrous tissues around the knuckles and wrists, responds well to copper supplements that are low-molecular-weight chelates.

"Consider one other aspect of copper in the stomach. In a study published in the *British Medical Journal* by Dr. C. Legon, it was reported that the incidence of stomach cancer in North Wales was linked to a copper deficiency. In soils that were

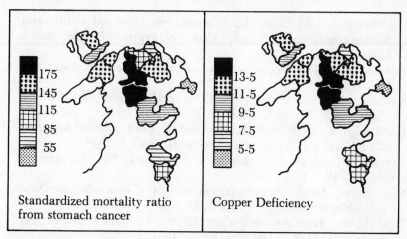

Standardized mortality ratio from stomach cancer

Copper Deficiency

Figure 11 – 1. **The uneven distribution of stomach cancer in North Wales compared with the distribution of soils with high organic matter content resulting in copper deficiencies.** SOURCE: K. Shutte, *The Biology of the Trace Elements* (Philadelphia: J.B. Lippincott, 1964), p. 122.

depleted of copper due to high organic matter there was a higher amount of cancer." (See Figure 11-1.)

"It appears from what you've said that copper may well play a role in the prevention and possibly even the treatment of ulcers and other ailments," said the lady. "I think I'll talk to my doctor again about how much copper I should be getting in my supplements, because it sounds like I can't really afford to be without it."

ADDITIONAL READING

Guthrie, H., *Introductory Nutrition* (St. Louis: Times Mirror/Mosby) 1986.

Coffey, R., "The inter-relationship of the immune response and trace element physiology," paper presented to the Subcommittee on Disease Research of National Cattlemen's Assoc., 1985.

Evered, D. and Lawrenson, G., eds., *Biological Roles of Copper* (Amsterdam: Excerpta Medica), 1980.

Hildebran, S. and Hunt, J., "Copper-responsive epiphysitis and tendon contracture in a foal," *Mod. Vet. Practice*, 67:268, March 1986.

Frieden, E., "The biochemistry of copper," *Scientific American*, May 1986.

Karcioglu, Z. and Sarper, R., *Zinc and Copper in Medicine* (Springfield: Charles C Thomas), 1980.

Hambridge, K. and Nichols, B., *Zinc and Copper in Clinical Nutrition* (New York: S.P. Medical and Scientific Books), 1978.

Everett, M., *Medical Biochemistry* (New York: Paul B. Hoeber, Inc.), 1946.

Sigel, H., ed., *Metal Ions in Biological Systems—Copper Proteins* (New York: Marcel Dekker), V. 13, 1981.

Sigel H., ed., *Metal Ions in Biological Systems—Properties of Copper* (New York: Marcel Dekker), V. 12, 1981.

Sorenson, J., "Some Copper Coordination Compounds and their antiinflammatory and antiulcer activities," *Inflammation*, 1:317, 1976.

Boyle, E., *et al.*, "The role of copper in preventing gastrointestinal damage to acidic antiflammatory drugs," *J. Pharm. Pharmocol.*, 28:865, 1976.

Graff, D., *et al.*, "Absorption of minerals compared with chelates made from various protein sources into rat jejunal slices, *in vitro*," paper given to Utah Academy of Arts, Letters, and Sciences, Salt Lake City, April 1970.

Legon, C., "The aetiological significance of geographical variations in cancer mortality," *Brit. Med. J.*, 700, 1952.

Voisin, A., *Soil Grass and Cancer* (London: Crosby Lockwood), 1959.

Schutte, K., *The Biology of the Trace Elements* (Philadelphia: J.B. Lippincott), 1964.

Kirstein, D. "Copper and Immune Response," Proceedings of Natural Animal Disease Center, Ames, Iowa, June 1, 1988, p. 25.

Iron
A Brief Introduction

I ron is probably the most widely recognized of all mineral nutrients, yet the lack of iron remains the number one deficiency problem in the United States. This situation is perplexing to some since iron is a rather common mineral in foods and is also relatively inexpensive as a supplement.

Iron is found primarily in the blood, but small amounts of iron are found in every cell's components—the nucleus, protoplasm, and enzymes. The presence of iron is largely responsible for the uptake of oxygen by the cells and promotes the use of oxygen in their life processes. Nearly all iron in the body exists in combination with protein whether in transport, storage, enzymes, or respiratory compounds.

Besides being essential in the formation of hemoglobin and red blood cells, iron plays an important role in proper bone formation, healing, RNA synthesis, skin and hair pigmentation, protein metabolism, and proper bone formation.

Approximately 70 percent of the iron in the body is considered functional iron, the majority of which is found in the hemoglobin molecule of the red blood cell. A small portion of iron is part of myoglobin in muscle while the rest of the functional iron is found in tissue enzymes and contributes to the process of cellular respiration.

When iron deficiencies exist, a person may exhibit a general weakness and anemia. He may have pale skin and abnormal fatigue as well as a shortness of breath. A lack of appetite may be present. There may be edema and skin sores.

Iron is poorly absorbed from the small intestine unless it is properly chelated with amino acids. When ingested as an inorganic salt generally only 4 to 6 percent is actually absorbed.

The National Research Council recommends a daily dietary allowance (RDA) of 10 mg for infants, 15 mg for children up to the age of six, 10 mg from the age of six to eleven, 18 mg for males from twelve to twenty-two, 10 mg for males twenty-three and older, 18 mg for females eleven to fifty, and 10 mg for females above fifty years of age.

12

The Roles of Iron in the Body

D uring a break in the nutrition conference lectures, I was introduced to an English physician who had expressed an interest in my work on minerals. After the introductions were made, he immediately commenced a vigorous verbal assault.

"I don't know why you are so concerned about minerals in the diet," he grumbled. "There is no such thing as a serious mineral deficiency in the United Kingdom, except under experimental conditions."

I recoiled slightly and then said, "I gather you don't consider anemia to be a serious problem."

"What do you mean?" he asked.

"As you know," I explained, "anemia is a deficiency of red blood cells that carry oxygen throughout the body. Anemia is often linked to a lack of enough iron to make hemoglobin for the essential oxygen-carrying part of the red blood cell. According to the World Health Organization, iron deficiency is the most prevalent mineral deficiency in the world. The American Medical Association estimates that 64 percent of all menstruating women in the United States are anemic to some degree. Further, Professor Ian Morton from Queen Elizabeth College in London stated that the Western diet provides from 10 to 15 mg of iron each day, but that less than 1 mg of that iron is actually absorbed by the body. The British government feels that a normal adult needs 12 mg of iron each day just to keep from becoming anemic, while the US government recommends about 18 mg as a daily dietary allowance. Professor Margaret Simko of New York University and her coworkers have written in their book *Nutrition Assessment* that iron deficiency anemia is the most common nutritional disorder in the world. According to Professor Simko, the deficiency can be the result of a lack of iron in the diet, excessive loss of iron from bleeding or menstruation, increased body requirements for iron, or impaired absorption of the dietary iron."

"I can understand greater requirements, excessive losses, or dietary deficiencies causing this type of anemia," responded the doctor, "but metabolism is a puzzling question. Why is absorption of iron so low?"

"Absorption of minerals is greatly influenced by the form in which they are taken into the body," I replied. "Let me give you an example. Suppose a person swallowed improperly chelated iron ascorbate. As far as the body is concerned, this form of iron is similar to inorganic iron sulfate. It is not a chelate the body can efficiently use in nutrition. Thus, in order to obtain the iron from this supplement, the body must first remove the ascorbate from the iron through a chemical process call ionization. The moment that happens, the body is left with an unstable mineral which can enter into many chemical reactions that naturally take place in the stomach and intestines. These reactions can bind the unstable mineral so tightly that it is no longer soluble and available for absorption by the body. Consequently, only a small percentage of the swallowed mineral is absorbed through the intestines. The rest is eliminated from the body as waste.

"In our book *Intestinal Absorption of Metal Ions and Chelates*, my colleagues and I have presented research that shows iron absorption in a normal person to range between 2 percent and 10 percent of the ingested amount, with 4 percent about average. Referring back to Professor Morton's data showing that our diets provide us with between 10 and 15 mg of iron a day and multiplying that amount by 4 percent, we can quickly calculate that the average person only absorbs between 0.4 and 0.6 mg of iron a day. Is it any wonder that iron deficiency is such a major problem around the world today?"

"Low absorption doesn't necessarily prove that iron deficiency is a major health problem, does it?" countered the Englishman.

I responded by telling him that in an address to the Association of Physicians of Malaysia, Dr. Lenard Mervyn, a British researcher who did much pioneering research on vitamin B_{12} and whom I mentioned in an earlier chapter, said that although iron deficiency anemia accounted for few deaths, it played an extremely important role in contributing to the general unhealthy condition and substandard performance of millions of people.

"How can a mineral deficiency have such a negative effect on the body?" inquired the doctor, showing more interest now than antagonism.

"The fact that iron chelated by specific chelating agents normally found in most healthy body cells accounts for much of its importance to the body," I answered. "As a chelate, iron is involved in the enzymes that help put together the DNA and RNA necessary for cell replication. When we suffer from iron deficiencies, our bodies cannot make new cells and thus even the status quo maintenance of our bodies is impaired. The American Medical Association has reported that anemia resulting from an iron deficiency in the blood is one of the major nutritional problems in the United States. That statistic alone is frightening, but when we consider that iron deficiencies occur in our cells long before we become anemic, these findings take on new significance. Research at Albion Laboratories suggests that a high percentage of people who lack adequate amounts of chelated iron in their bodies are still not clinically anemic."

"Exactly what types of health problems can be associated with anemia?" asked the doctor.

"Dr. Hal Hopson and I published part of the answer to your question in a medical magazine in which we noted significant reductions in the incidence of infectious diseases in experimental animals which were not anemic. We found that animals challenged with *E. coli* bacteria were particularly resistant to that species of microorganism when they had adequate amounts of iron in their bodies. Without sufficient iron, these same animals became sick."

"It sounds like an interesting laboratory animal experiment," commented the doctor, "but what about studies involving iron deficiency anemia in humans?"

"I recall just such an example," I responded. "Dr. H.M. Mackay reported that the number of cases of bronchitis and gastroenteritis of anemic people in London decreased when these people received iron supplements. Further, other researchers found that certain types of skin infections are common in individuals suffering from an iron deficiency. Their skin lesions cleared up rapidly when they took iron supplements. In other studies, researchers concluded that the body's ability to develop an immunity to disease was significantly impaired if there was an iron deficiency present."

I then showed this physician a report published by the World Health Organization. The WHO found that people who have iron deficiency anemia tend to have more frequent illnesses. After reading the paper, the doctor had a concerned look on his face.

"I'm a physician," he explained. "When an individual comes to me with an illness, I usually treat him or her with drugs. What you're suggesting is that if I concentrated on certain nutritional programs, I may be able to prevent the disease-causing organism from getting a foothold in the body." I nodded in agreement.

"Why do you think there is such a close correlation between iron deficiency anemia and poor health?" he asked.

I explained to him that for the white blood cells to destroy the harmful bacteria and other disease-causing pathogens in the body, the white blood cells must have adequate iron. "There is an enzyme called myeloperoxidase which makes it possible for white blood cells to ingest and destroy bacteria," I said. "But that enzyme won't work unless it contains iron to activate it. The role of iron in this enzyme is rather like the role of spark plugs in an automobile. If the spark plugs are removed, even though fuel is present, the automobile won't run. The motor needs the spark plugs to initiate the combustion, just as certain enzymes need specific minerals to initiate the necessary chemical reactions. Thus, if the body is iron deficient (anemic), the white blood cells don't have enough iron to activate the myeloperoxidase enzyme, and the disease-causing bacteria cannot be destroyed naturally by the body. This is frequently the case in an anemic person."

"So an adequate supply of iron is important in fighting bacterial diseases," said the doctor, "but what about viral infections?"

"As a doctor, you know that the body is capable of maintaining a defense mechanism against most forms of illness as long as the proper ammunition is in good supply. To defend against attack by viruses, the body cells manufacture protective coatings called glycoproteins. Glycoproteins are produced inside the cell and then transferred to the cell's exterior, where they act as a shield against viral attacks."

I noticed that the Englishman's interest had been piqued, so I continued. "Simply stated, glycoproteins are formed when the sugars galactose and glucose are combined with the amino acid lysine in the cell. The catch is that these sugars and the amino acids cannot be bonded together in the cell except in the presence of properly chelated iron, manganese, and vitamin C. If any one of these nutrients is missing or severely depleted, the production of glycoproteins is retarded and the uncoated cells become vulnerable to invasion by the virus.

"In my opinion, one of the reasons Dr. Linus Pauling's work on vitamin C is so controversial is because everyone concentrates on the effect of the vitamin with little or no regard for the other nutrients necessary to make vitamin C effective in preventing viral infections. When other researchers can't duplicate Dr. Pauling's findings, the inconsistency may be the result of an absent or deficient nutrient which is needed for the vitamin C to function effectively."

"What you're saying," interrupted the doctor, "is that the vitamin C that many people take as protection against the common cold won't do any good without sufficient amounts of properly chelated iron and manganese."

"That's exactly what current research is suggesting," I agreed, taking a book from my briefcase. "Professor Helen

Guthrie has summarized the functions of iron in her book *Introductory Nutrition*. She says:

> There is considerable evidence that iron is important in many functions other than those associated with blood formation and the transport of oxygen. These non-heme functions include catalyzing the conversion of beta-carotene (the precursor of vitamin A) to vitamin A; the synthesis of purines, an integral part of nucleic acid; clearance of blood lipids; collagen synthesis; antibody production; and detoxification of drugs in the liver. Studies of the role of iron as an anti-infective agent suggest that although iron is necessary for the growth of microorganisms, it is an essential part of enzymes and immune substances needed to destroy invading infectious organisms. Lactoferrin in breast milk is an iron-containing substance especially effective against E. coli organisms in the gastrointestinal tract of infants.[1]

"These data substantiate findings which Dr. Hopson and I published."

"I admit that I wasn't aware of the far-reaching effects that iron deficiencies might have on the body," conceded the doctor. "But I don't believe that the problem is all that widespread."

"In the United States," I responded, "a government report addressed this question by relating anemia to job productivity and mortality. The study concluded that if Americans corrected the nutritional anemia affecting them, general job productivity would increase .5 percent and 25 percent of lost workdays due to illness would be eliminated. The report also showed that mortality associated with anemia could be reduced by 25 percent if nutrition were improved. These findings correlate closely with studies I have done in which survival rates of experimental animals were improved by 24 percent when the animals received iron supplements in a metabolizable form such as an amino acid chelate. Similar tests using nonchelated or improperly chelated iron supplements were much less effective in improving longevity of the animals.

"Furthermore, I've read reports by the British government

that reflect their concern with iron deficiency in the United Kingdom. In 1953 a law was passed requiring the addition of iron to all white flour to replace the iron lost during the milling process. However, in 1970 the Royal Society of Medicine reported that supplementing bread with iron was of no value because the iron additive was in a form that couldn't be absorbed."

"Here we are back to the absorption problem again," said the doctor. "What was wrong with the iron added to the white flour?"

"Well," I explained, "iron generally functions in the body as an amino acid chelate. Research has shown that our bodies must convert most forms of swallowed iron into a chelated form before we can utilize the iron. Unless the iron is correctly chelated, it has no biological effect on the body, and we would be just as iron deficient as if we had not swallowed any iron at all. Chelation does not guarantee absorption by itself, because proper chelation is a technical process and must be controlled carefully to make the iron biologically useful."

"How can absorption of iron be affected by other foods in our diet?" questioned the doctor.

"Remember what I said earlier," I reminded. "Only an average of 4 percent of the iron we ingest is actually absorbed unless it is properly chelated. With nonchelated iron, if we eat large quantities of dairy products, such as milk or cheese, these foods can decrease the amount of dietary iron that is available to the body by chemically attaching to the nonchelated iron, thus making it unavailable for use by the body.

"I remember talking with another physician who had a patient that was suffering from iron deficiency anemia although he was taking iron supplements. Puzzled by this, the doctor conducted several tests on his anemic patient. Ultimately he learned that his patient was consuming huge amounts of milk each day, and the excessive consumption was interfering with the normal iron absorption program of the body. When the milk intake was reduced, the anemia went away.

"Not only are dairy products a negative factor in iron absorption, but so also are other foods or drugs that reduce the acidity of the stomach and intestines, such as antacids. Foods such as wheat bran will also reduce iron bioavailability because of the phytic acid in the bran. Low protein levels and too much copper, calcium, or phosphorus in the diet have a negative effect on iron absorption. Following a vegetarian diet may inhibit iron absorption because the vegetables are lower in heme iron and contain higher fiber and phytic acid. Fiber, as you know, will bind with iron in the stomach and intestines, rendering the iron insoluble and thus unavailable. Availability of iron is such a major nutritional problem that in 1982 the American Chemical Society held a conference devoted to the subject."

"In that case," argued the doctor, "why not simply increase the amount of iron taken into the body? That way, there would be no question about how much is or is not available, because, in theory, there would be enough total iron in the diet to provide what is needed."

"That's not necessarily the answer," I countered. "Both British and American research have established that because of the interference of other substances, the body usually can't efficiently chelate enough iron to meet its optimum needs. A special iron-binding glycoprotein fraction containing 85 percent carbohydrate and 15 percent polypeptide is needed to chelate the iron in the gastric environment. For example, 4 percent to 6 percent of the iron is generally absorbed from iron sulfate, a common iron supplement that is used as the standard for measuring absorption performance of other iron. Additional research done at a university in cooperation with Albion Laboratories has shown that only about one-half of the absorbed iron from that iron sulfate is utilized by the body. The rest is eliminated into the lower bowel. Continued increases in the amount of iron from nonchelated sources can easily result in a state of iron toxicity in the intestines."

I asked the doctor, "How much iron would you absorb into your system if you swallowed a rusty nail?"

"Not much at all," he smiled.

"The reason you wouldn't is because the body has to convert, or chelate, that iron into a metabolizable form before absorption can take place. Research has shown that intestinal absorption of iron varies significantly depending on the chemical form of the ingested iron. In university absorption studies, when the iron was properly prechelated with amino acids, its absorption was 360 percent better than iron carbonate, 380 percent better than iron sulfate, and 490 percent better than iron oxide, which is what the rusty nail is. Those tests were conducted in the laboratory under ideal conditions. In a normal situation, the percentage differences would have been greater because intestinal absorption of the inorganic forms of iron would have been decreased by the interferences present in the stomach and intestines. Consequently, it makes sense to ingest this special iron amino acid chelate if iron supplementation is desired and one wishes to maximize iron absorption. Simply swallowing nonchelated minerals to run them through the body is an exercise in futility."

At this point, we seemed to have reached agreement and so we changed the subject to another research project in which we were both interested.

NOTES

1. H. Guthrie, *Introductory Nutrition* (St. Louis: C.V. Mosby Co., 1975), p. 147.

ADDITIONAL READING

Guthrie, H., *Introductory Nutrition* (St. Louis: Times Mirror/ Mosby College Publishing), 1986.

Morton, I., "How mineral deficient are we?" paper given at an Albion symposium, London, England, April 1976.

Simko, M., *et al.*, *Nutrition Assessment* (Rockville: Aspen Systems Corp.), 1984.

Ashmead, D., "The need for chelated trace minerals," *Vet. Med./ Small Animal Clinic.*, 68:467, April, 1974.

Ashmead, H.D., *et al.*, *Intestinal Absorption of Metal Ions and Chelates* (Springfield: Charles C Thomas), 1985.

Mervyn, L., "The clinical significance of chelated minerals as nutritional supplements in medical practice," paper given to the Association of Physicians of Malaysia, 1982.

Porter, R. and Fitzsimons, D., eds., *Iron Metabolism* (Amsterdam: Elsevier), 1977.

Bezkoravaing, A., *Biochemistry of Nonheme Iron* (New York: Plenum Press), 1980.

Dunford, H., *et al.*, eds., *The Biological Chemistry of Iron* (Dordrecht, Holland: D. Reidel Publishing Co.), 1982.

Hopson, H. and Ashmead, D., "Iron deficiencies and their relationship to infectious diseases," *Vet. Medicine/Small Animal Clinic.*, 71:809, June 1976.

Mackay, H., "Anaemia in infancy: Its prevalence and prevention," *Arch. Dis. Childh.*, 3:117, 1928.

Ashmead, D., ed., *Chelated Mineral Nutrition in Plants, Animals and Man* (Springfield: Charles C Thomas), 1982.

Ashmead, D. and Beck, B., "Chelated minerals and cancer," paper given at the annual meeting of Cancer Victims and Friends, Los Angeles, 1978.

Weir, C., *Benefits from Human Nutrition Research: Human Nutrition Report No. 2* (Washington, DC: US Department of Agriculture), 1978.

Ashmead, H., *et al.*, "Chelation does not guarantee mineral metabolism," *J. Appl. Nutr.*, 26:5, Summer 1974.

Ashmead, H. and Ashmead, D., "By the way, it's chelated," *World Health & Ecology News*, 7:8, 1979.

Ashmead, D., "Chelation in nutrition," *World Health & Ecology News*, 7:10, 1976.

Graff, D., *et al.*, "Absorption of minerals compared with chelates made from various protein sources into rat jejunal slices, *in vitro*," paper given to Utah Academy of Arts, Letters, and Sciences, Salt Lake City, 1970.

Webb, J., *et al.*, "Spectroscopic and magnetic studies of iron III," *Biochemistry* 12:265, 1973.

Mervyn, L., *Beat the Iron Crisis* (Wellingborough, Northants: Thorsons Publishers Limited), 1988.

Lead
A Brief Introduction

A lthough some researchers still feel that lead may be an essential trace element in human nutrition, the majority look at this metal as a contaminant. While lead will activate some enzyme systems in the body, in most instances it can be replaced by other minerals without physiological or biochemical upset. Lead is found in the tissues of our bodies. Nevertheless, in this book it will be considered a poison.

Lead poisoning is probably one of the most rapidly increasing environmentally related diseases we see today! Smoking increases one's daily lead intake by 25 percent. Lead replaces deficient calcium in the bone, so a high-calcium diet will prevent such a deposition. It also affects magnesium levels and interferes with the normal metabolism of iron.

13

Toxic Air: Trying to Live with It

As a colleague and I drove along a mountain highway which opened into a sprawling valley metropolis, I commented on the haze of pollution which hung over the city.

"It looks like this valley is suffering from malnutrition," I said wryly, hoping for a rise out of my drowsy traveling companion. We had been on a speaking engagement in California and were returning home.

"What makes you say that?" questioned my friend, sitting up enough to take note of where we were.

"Can't you see the cloud of pollution hanging over this valley?" I asked, eager to begin a conversation. "The people who breathe that air could well be bringing upon themselves many of the symptoms and conditions of malnutrition."

"I think you'll have to explain that a little further," responded my friend. "I'm not alert enough at the moment to pick up on your riddles and semantic exercises."

"I'll be happy to explain if you'll reach into my briefcase and find that publication of the American Medical Association's Council on Nutrition. They give a definition of malnutrition that I think you will find interesting," I said, as we continued along the freeway.

"This must be the one you mean," said my friend, sorting through some papers. "Their definition of malnutrition reads: 'A state of impaired functional ability of deficient structural integrity of development brought about by a discrepancy between the supply to the body tissues of essential nutrients and calories, and the biologic demand for them.'"

123

"Based on this definition, any agent that interferes with the supply of nutrients to the body with a resulting deficiency causes malnutrition. A few years after the AMA published its definition of malnutrition, Dr. Carl Pfeiffer attempted to break down the agents causing malnutrition into seven categories in his book *Mental and Elemental Nutrients*. The first cause of malnutrition he identified was a contamination of soils resulting in nutritionally deficient crops. Poverty ranked as the second reason for malnutrition. Medical factors such as malabsorption were listed as the third agent, with improper food storage a fourth and contaminated food a fifth cause. Contamination included mercury poisoning in sea fish, as well as the use of mercury-containing fungicides to treat the grain we eat."

"According to Dr. Pfeiffer," commented my friend, "malnutrition has many sources."

"In this same book," I continued, "he goes on to list food processing, such as grain refining, as the sixth cause of malnutrition. Seventh on his list of contributors to malnutrition is the poisoning of water through excess toxicants such as lead, cadmium, or nitrates."

"That appears to be a thorough analysis of the various possible causes of malnutrition in our supposedly advanced society," my friend added with some concern.

"Dr. Pfeiffer's breakdown of the basic causes of malnutrition is excellent," I agreed. "But I think that it lacks at least one cause which today is probably far more devastating to humankind than many of the contributing factors which he listed. In fact, we're driving through it as well as contributing to it at this moment by our automobile exhaust, and that is air pollution."

"You mean to say that dirty air contributes significantly to malnutrition in this country?" exclaimed my friend, rolling up the car window.

"We don't often think of the air as inducing malnutrition, do we?" I asked rhetorically. "Yet few would disagree that breathing the smog-laden air in most large cities throughout the country is unhealthy. In study after study, smoking has been linked to cardiovascular disease, lung and throat cancer, and fetal abnormalities including death. Yet in one sense smoking is nothing more than breathing another form of polluted air."

"What is the actual physiology of the ill effects of polluted air on our bodies?" questioned my friend.

"What happens," I explained, "is that breathing poor quality air interferes with the body's ability to obtain needed nutrients because the toxic chemicals in the air can create many forms of malabsorption or they can contribute to the body's imbalance of certain nutrients. When these toxicants interfere with the body's nutritional well-being, they fall within the AMA's definition of malnutrition."

"But isn't that merely a clinical definition of malnutrition?" asked my friend. "Is this type of malnutrition really a threat to the health of our society?"

"After years of intensive study at the University of Alabama and elsewhere, Professor Emanual Cheraskin and his associates in their book *Diet and Disease* concluded that most, if not all, disease is at least indirectly related to malnutrition. If this is true, and I suspect it is, then even slight evidence of malnutrition is cause for concern in protecting and preserving our good health. And the malnutrition caused by breathing toxic air could be a significant stumbling block in maintaining an acceptable living environment."

"Can you explain how a disease might be related to malnutrition," said my friend. "I want to be able to explain this idea to my medical associates."

"To illustrate what diseases might result, keep in mind that smoking increases the need for vitamins A and C. Vitamin A is essential among other things for proper visual functioning, synthesis of steroid metabolites in the body, and stabilization of cellular and intracellular membranes. Vitamin C is essential for oxidation reduction reactions in the body and synthesis of collagen and elastin. A deficiency of these two nutrients frequently results in alteration of the respiratory organs of the body."

"But if I don't smoke," retorted my friend, "then I shouldn't be concerned about those deficiencies, should I?"

"Do you remember a few years ago when Mount St. Helens in Washington became an active volcano and erupted?" My friend nodded. "In the aftermath of the eruption, Albion Laboratories contacted people in Washington and Oregon who had previously used Albion for some clinical work and asked them to participate in a follow-up study. The mineral levels in their tissues were already on file as a result of the previous work. We asked them to submit additional tissue samples for analysis; most did. The new analyses were compared to their old records. In comparing their contaminant tissue levels to their earlier levels, we found cadmium was twelve times the normal level; mercury was three times higher; nickel was twenty times higher; and lead levels had increased by four times. Presumably they had incorporated these toxic metals into their body tissues by breathing the ash-laden air after the volcanic eruption. Given these findings, I think you would be surprised at the variety and quantity of pollutants in the air that we breathe," I replied as we continued our drive into the city.

"In 1972 my father, Dr. Harvey Ashmead, published an article in the *Journal of Applied Nutrition* where he reported that motor vehicles in the United States expel 86,190,000 tons of pollutants into the air each year. You would expect that these pollutants would be confined to areas immediately adjacent to large metropolitan centers, but you must remember that these toxicants are airborne and subject to various atmospheric conditions. Once they are picked up by the clouds and air currents, these pollutants are spread over the earth. When it rains and snows, these minute particles are redeposited on the earth, where they can contaminate anything they touch."

"Aren't you just assuming that these pollutants may fall indiscriminately over the earth?" questioned my friend. "What evidence do you have to support the idea that these toxic elements are contaminating anything but the most densely populated areas of the world?"

"I agree that more densely populated areas have greater pollution," I answered. "In one study which I participated in we drove across the United States collecting vegetation samples every one hundred miles. Chemical analysis revealed that lead contents of these samples were directly related to the population and industrial environment from which the vegetation was taken. But to answer your question more directly, in one of my father's research programs," I recalled, "pure white snow on the lofty mountain peaks of Utah was assayed for heavy metals. Taken at various elevations up to 7,000 feet above sea level, the study showed that lead, among other pollutants, was being deposited from the atmosphere in frightening amounts. When that mountain snow melts, it carries the dissolved pollutants with it into the drinking water of both humans and animals. These toxic materials also end up in the streams and ditches from which farmers draw their irrigation water.

"To illustrate how serious this problem is, our research scientists analyzed the tissues of deer and elk taken from these mountains, animals that had lived all of their lives thousands of feet above the visible pollution in valleys below. These animals had an average of 250 ppm of lead in their hair and, between 20 and 30 micrograms of lead in every 100 grams of liver. As far as I am aware, lead has no known positive biological function; as a result of airborne contaminants placed there by humans, these wild animals were being poisoned."

"What about the contamination of the water used for irrigation and the direct pollution of the soil and foliage?" asked my rather concerned friend. "Have there been any studies to determine the extent of air pollution's effect on agriculture?"

"In another study," I answered, "it was found that corn grown in a midwestern state averaged 5 ppm of lead. Soybeans had 4 ppm of lead, and alfalfa contained 3 ppm.

"The critical question then becomes," I continued, "what happens to a man when he eats poultry, beef, or pork that has consumed these polluted feeds, or if he is a strict vegetarian, what happens when he eats these polluted plants even if they are grown organically? The answer is obvious: he also takes the contaminants into his body."

My friend was silent for a long time before he finally spoke. "What you are telling me is that we have all been exposed to the effects of the toxic air around us no matter how careful we are, and we are most likely suffering from some form or degree of malnutrition as a result."

"I wish it weren't true," I confessed, "but many of these harmful pollutants are reaching a majority of human beings and it is affecting our quality of life. In an article published in *Psychology Today*, University of Virginia psychologists, James Pennebaker and Darren Newtson, concluded that people living within ninety miles of the Mount St. Helens volcano were suffering from what they believed was a psychological disorder called misattribution reaction. These people blamed the volcano for all their problems from stomachaches to marital discord. Personally, I believe there were biochemical malfunctions resulting from heavy metal contamination, which we had found in our research mentioned earlier. These disturbances interfered with proper enzymatic functions, which manifested themselves as physiological problems, as well as the psychological problems the researchers recognized. Let me illustrate it this way: Today, what is considered a normal amount of lead and mercury expected to be found in various human tissue samples would have been considered a toxic level only a few years ago. Both these minerals are contaminants that contribute to malnutrition. In fact, according to the late Dr. Henry Schroeder in his book *The Poisons Around Us*, the number of diseases which these and other heavy metals are responsible for is frightening."

"What can be done about our polluted environment?" questioned my friend. "Or how can we minimize the effects of these toxic materials on us?"

"Both questions are valid," I replied. "Of course the simplistic answer is to clean up the air and water. The environmentalists are taking steps to do that, but their success is limited and must be balanced with economic considerations. Being careful in our selection of foods is another precaution. However, the avoidance of pesticides or synthetic fertilizers does not guarantee that the food we eat is low in other toxicants such as lead, mercury, or cadmium."

"So are we caught in an irreversible tailspin of industry-induced self-destruction?" asked my friend with a rather melodramatic gesture.

"I don't think it's that hopeless," I reassured my friend. "There are ways to counteract the negative effects on the body of chemically induced malnutrition. Dr. Daphne Roe, in her book *Drug-Induced Nutritional Deficiencies,* states that increased intake of certain nutrients such as vitamins and minerals has been found to be effective in overcoming these types of malnutrition. The same principles apply in the treatment of atmospheric chemical pollution. Several studies have been conducted which support the idea that supplementation of vitamins and minerals can go a long way toward overcoming the deficiencies which are created when toxic elements enter the body. Dr. Roe suggests a systematic supplementation of the nutrients which have proven to be most sensitive to induced deficiencies. These include folate and other B vitamins, which tend to be easily depleted, as do vitamins A and E. Minerals such as calcium, magnesium, zinc, and iron should also be supplemented, according to Dr. Roe."

"Are you saying that supplementation is the answer to overcoming the toxic air that we breathe?" questioned my friend.

"All I'm saying is that short of leaving the planet Earth, it's probably the best defense that we have," I replied. "Of course, we must continue to prevent what pollution we can by regulating the air quality as strictly as possible, but we must be more aware of the positive effects which vitamin and mineral supplements can have in helping our bodies to counteract these toxicants."

"I think that I will re-examine my supplement program when we get home," said my friend, slumping into his seat. "I certainly wouldn't want to be a victim of malnutrition as a result of the air I breathe."

ADDITIONAL READING

Pfeiffer, C., *Mental and Elemental Nutrients* (New Canaan: Keats Publishing Inc.), 1975.

Cheraskin, E., *et al.*, *Diet and Disease* (New Canaan: Keats Publishing Inc.), 1977.

Ashmead, H., "Ecology, chelation and animal experimentation," *J. Appl. Nutr.*, 24:8, Spring 1972.

Ashmead, H., "Atmospheric metal pollution", a paper given at the 17th annual National Health Federation Convention, Los Angeles, January 1972.

Feedstuffs, "Decline in trace minerals in grain shown," 41:7, August 9, 1969.

Psychology Today, "The volcano as a scapegoat," 15:33, January 1981.

Schroeder, H., *The Poisons Around Us* (New Canaan: Keats Publishing, Inc.), 1979

Roe, D., *Drug-Induced Nutritional Deficiencies* (Westport: The AVI Publishing Co., Inc.), 1976.

Ashmead, H. and Fouad, T., "Trace mineral inter-relationships, new techniques of detecting lead and other heavy metals in animals, and the role of organic chelated trace minerals play as enzyme catalysts," paper given at Oklahoma Veterinary Medical convention, Tulsa, February 1971.

Magnesium
A Brief Introduction

M agnesium has only recently officially been recognized as an essential mineral nutrient in the body. Magnesium is necessary for synthesis of certain amino acids, activation of many enzyme systems, maintenance of DNA and RNA, and normal contraction of muscles.

One of the most vital muscles in the body, the heart, is dependent upon magnesium for proper functioning. The heartbeat is begun when the nerve impulse reaches the thin filament on the heart muscle cell known as actin. Calcium provides the stimulus for the actin to reach magnetic-like action toward the cell, thus creating a contraction. Magnesium then comes into play by repelling the calcium and relaxing the muscle cell. Without magnesium, the proper contracting and relaxing of the heart muscle would be impaired.

Magnesium also aids in the elimination of foreign matter and waste from the body; it builds lung and nervous tissue cells; it gives strength to bones and teeth; and it helps regulate blood pH.

Magnesium is absorbed from the small intestine. Absorption is approximately 25 percent to 30 percent of the ingested amount, if the magnesium is relatively soluble. The uptake of magnesium amino acid chelate (if properly chelated) is at least 1.8 times greater than magnesium carbonate, 2.6 times greater than magnesium sulfate, and 4.1 times greater than magnesium oxide.

131

Recommended dietary allowances (RDA) for magnesium as established by the National Research Council are 50 mg per day for infants, 70 mg per day for children up to three years of age, 200 mg for children from four to six, 250 mg per day for children seven to ten years of age, 350 mg per day for males from eleven to fourteen years, 400 mg for males from fifteen to eighteen years of age, 350 mg per day for all males over the age of eighteen, and 300 mg per day for females eleven and older. During pregnancy and lactation the dosage should be increased by 150 mg per day.

If the diet is deficient in magnesium or if the absorption of dietary magnesium is low, symptoms of that deficiency may include excessive irritability of nerves and muscles, including nervous tics and twitches, and apprehensiveness, brain and body exhaustion, confusion, disorientation and irritability, irregular heartbeat, poor circulation and pale complexions, convulsions, seizures, tremors, and finally glandular disturbances.

14

Chelated Magnesium
The Natural Tranquilizer

Upon my return from some business meetings in Minnesota, I kept an appointment with my personal physician for a physical examination. While waiting in his office, I began reading the label on a sample bottle of tranquilizers left by a salesman. Observing my interest in the new medication, the doctor remarked, "That's the third new tranquilizer I've seen on the market in the past two months. Because so many of my patients seem to need a drug to calm their nerves, I'm glad to see new types of tranquilizers being developed. How do you account for the increase over the past few years in the need for more and better tranquilizers?"

Knowing that our medical philosophies often differed, I was surprised that he was interested in my opinion. However, sensing his genuine concern over what he saw as a major health problem, I responded candidly. "One reason I see for the recent proliferation of tranquilizers is the increasing prominence of vitamin and mineral deficiencies in the foods we eat, particularly magnesium."

My doctor looked up from the examination form he was completing and questioned, "What do you mean by a magnesium deficiency?"

If the doctor had wanted to get rid of me, he had asked the wrong question. My recent business in Minnesota had included speaking at a medical convention, where I addressed the topic of magnesium in the diet. Because of the research being done at Albion Laboratories, I had collected a great deal of infor-

133

mation about magnesium deficiencies, and I was anxious to share my findings with him and anyone else who would listen.

"Look at the foods we eat today," I said in answer to the doctor's question. "In a four-year study on crops grown in eleven midwestern states, researchers found that the overall mineral content declined from year to year during the tests. One thousand samples of various crops were taken from the farms in these states the first year. Each successive year, a sample was taken from the same farm in the same field. All of the crop samples were assayed for their mineral contents by atomic absorption spectrophotometry. This study found that the magnesium content of the corn, for example, decreased 22 percent over the four years. [The other minerals also declined, as shown in Table 14-1.] Other studies have confirmed that many of our foods do not contain the same amounts of minerals as previously thought."

"What accounts for the specific loss in magnesium content of these plants?" the doctor wanted to know.

"Well, I know that you do a little gardening," I said. "What type of fertilizer do you normally use?"

"Usually one that has a high N-P-K rating," said the doctor, "that is, high in nitrogen, phosphorus, and potassium."

"Most farmers are using similar types of fertilizer in their large commercial operations," I explained. "However, studies have shown that generally higher and higher amounts of N-P-K fertilizers must be used to achieve consistent crop yields from year to year. The increase in the K, or potassium, portion of the fertilizer has a direct bearing on the magnesium content of the crops. This fact was made known as early as 1953 when a Frenchman, D. Mulder, reported at an international agricultural convention that potassium had been shown to be antagonistic to magnesium. This means that as more potassium is applied to the soil, the plant in turn absorbs that high level of potassium, which interferes with the plant's ability to absorb magnesium. Magnesium in the natural chelated form is actually the cornerstone of the chlorophyll molecule, which is essential for plant photosynthesis. After a certain point, the

Table 14-1. Decline of Trace Elements in Corn

		Beginning	Ending
Calcium	− 41%	.047%	.025%
Phosphorus	− 8%	.26%	.24%
Potassium	− 28%	.34%	.245%
Sodium	− 55%	.022%	.01%
Magnesium	− 22%	.128%	.10%
Iron	− 26%	21.20 ppm	15.70 ppm
Copper	− 68%	2.56 ppm	.82 ppm
Zinc	− 10%	22.01 ppm	19.90 ppm
Manganese	− 34%	4.88 ppm	3.23 ppm

higher the potassium in the soil, the less magnesium the plant is able to absorb and utilize. Consequently, I'm afraid that in our effort to maintain high crop yields through abuse of N-P-K fertilizers, we may be growing magnesium-deficient plants. One indication of this magnesium deficiency may be the increased need for medications such as these new tranquilizers."

My doctor leaned back in his chair and commented, "I'll buy your concept about possible magnesium deficiencies in plants due to improper fertilization, but what does a magnesium deficiency have to do with my prescribing more tranquilizers?"

For an answer to the doctor's question, I referred him to a book by Dr. Helen Guthrie entitled *Introductory Nutrition* in which she wrote:

Magnesium . . . is one of the minerals involved in providing the proper environment in the extracellular fluid of nerve cells to promote the conduction of nerve impulses and to allow normal muscular contraction. In this situation, magnesium and calcium play antagonistic roles, calcium acting as a stimulator and magnesium as a relaxor substance. The relaxing effect of magnesium is evident from the fact that with increasing levels of the mineral in the blood,

there is an increasing anesthetic effect. . . . On the other
hand, low serum magnesium levels are associated with irritability, nervousness, and convulsions as the result of stim-
ulation of nerve impulses and increased muscular contraction.[1]

I went on to explain further that, according to Jerry Aikowa,
a medical doctor who is also a professor at the University of
Colorado, normally the nerve, when it is at rest, is surrounded
by calcium and magnesium. When the nerve is stimulated, the
magnesium and calcium are removed through chelation and
replaced by sodium and potassium. The calcium and magnesium then play the roles described by Professor Guthrie. As
long as the nerve goes on activating the muscle, the sodium
and potassium surround it. When the nerve is at rest, the sodium
and potassium are replaced by magnesium and calcium. This
mineral exchange happens in just fractions of a second.

"One of the problems resulting from the mineral exchange
around the nerve," I continued, "is that in a magnesium deficient state, the sodium and potassium may have a tendency to
remain around the nerve even when it is supposed to be at rest,
but since these two minerals are the 'exciting' minerals, the
nerves don't have a chance to rest. The excited nerves continue
to activate muscular movement, which may be diagnosed as
irritability or nervous tension. The usual method of treatment
with tranquilizers simply forms a temporary short circuit of
the nervous system without ever really solving the problem."

My doctor appeared to be quite interested in what I had
told him, and since the noon hour was near, he suggested we
go to lunch together and finish our discussion over what he
jokingly called "a plate of mineral-deficient food."

Once we had been shown to a relatively secluded table in a
nearby restaurant, the doctor said, "You mentioned in my office
earlier that you have been doing some research on nervous
conditions in animals. What studies have you done relating
nervous disorders to magnesium deficiencies?"

After the waitress took our orders, I told the doctor about
one experimental study in which our laboratory participated

involving a group of valuable race horses that were being treated by a veterinarian in California.

"The veterinarian working with these forty thoroughbreds was responsible for seeing that they were in top physical condition," I explained. "Their combined value was over ten million dollars, so money was no object in taking care of them. At one point in his care of the animals, the veterinarian noted that twenty-three of the forty horses showed signs of greater than normal nervousness, and since he was familiar with some of the research that Albion Laboratories had been doing, he consulted our laboratory. He wondered if we could suggest anything to help his animals calm down, short of pumping them full of drugs. After some rather extensive analysis of various tissue and blood samples, our scientists were able to determine that the horses which were demonstrating excessive excitability all showed noticeably lower levels of magnesium in their bodies than did the horses that appeared less excitable. We theorized that if some of the horses were actually suffering from acute magnesium deficiencies the nerves of these affected animals could possibly be deprived of the soothing effects of adequate amounts magnesium. Without sufficient magnesium, the nerves would have a tendency to continue to be excited, which meant nervous horses.

"After forming our theory, we asked the veterinarian to rank the twenty-three horses according to the degree of nervousness each animal exhibited. When we compared his ranking to our analytical findings, we found that they correlated closely. Those animals which were the most nervous had the greatest degree of magnesium deficiency. The calmer the horse, the higher the level of magnesium in the body. Those animals which were considered normal all had magnesium levels at the top of the measuring scale."

"What did the veterinarian do after he found out about the magnesium deficiency?" asked the doctor.

"One of the animal specialists from our laboratory with whom he was consulting suggested using a mineral supplement in which the magnesium was chelated with amino acids.

The veterinarian chose that form of magnesium because university research had previously shown that intestinal absorption of this particular chelate was 260 percent better than magnesium sulfate, 180 percent better than magnesium carbonate, and 410 percent better than magnesium oxide. Shortly after the addition of this highly absorbable form of magnesium supplement to the animals' feed, the veterinarian reported to us that all but two of the twenty-three excitable horses had become, in his words, 'noticeably more manageable.'"

"Based on what you have told me," said my doctor, "I suspect that much research has been done on animals to establish the beneficial effects of magnesium in dealing with nervous problems, but what do you know about the application of magnesium to human nervous disorders?"

I spent the remainder of the meal discussing published reports by numerous doctors who had used magnesium supplements as a means of dealing with patients suspected of suffering from clinical ailments related to nerves. I mentioned that, according to some of those medical reports, several doctors experienced excellent results in treating certain nervous disorders with magnesium supplementation.

"I've read some of those reports," added the doctor, "and one problem expressed by one research group was consistency of results. Some patients responded remarkably well to the magnesium treatments, while others showed little improvement in their nervous conditions."

"Do you recall," I asked, "that several different forms of magnesium were given during the tests without trying to distinguish between the effectiveness of each different supplement? In my opinion, it was a mistake to compare the results of research from magnesium carbonate to magnesium oxide to amino acid chelates of magnesium and then try to evaluate the results as if all the magnesium supplements were the same. Results will vary as intestinal absorption varies. Nonchelated magnesium requires the presence of specific carrier molecules in the intestine in order to be absorbed, whereas magnesium amino acid chelate (when properly chelated) is absorbed as part of a protein molecule. I'm sure you can recall hearing me talk about the importance of mineral absorption before, and these magnesium tests were a prime example of how different levels of absorption can produce different levels of effectiveness in dealing with problems such as nervous tension."

"So, based on the work done on the horses as well as other research, you feel that if the tests had been conducted using certain magnesium amino acid chelates as the only magnesium supplement that the results would have shown a more consistent reduction in nervous disorders?"

"Exactly," I exclaimed. "But even though we have centered our discussion around nerves, let's not pigeonhole magnesium as a mineral to be used only in calming nerves, because it has many other uses in the body. Magnesium has been found to be an activator for hundreds of enzymes that are produced within the body, each of them with an important function contributing to the control of a wide variety of metabolic processes. Among the functions that magnesium helps to regulate is protein synthesis."

"I guess I didn't realize that magnesium was such a basic building block in the body," interrupted my doctor.

"As you might know," I continued, "all body tissues are continually wearing out and being replaced. In order to synthesize new proteins to replace those that are worn out, the body must maintain adequate levels of magnesium to activate many of the enzymes involved. If our systems are deficient in magnesium, tissue replacement is slowed and sometimes falters. With a severe magnesium deficiency, the body could actually manifest accelerated signs of aging.

"Another important area in which our bodies require chelated magnesium is the proper regulation of calcium. Magnesium influences where calcium goes throughout the body and how it performs its wide range of vital functions, including the nerves, which we have talked about. It is common knowledge that we need plenty of calcium to have strong bones and teeth, but without magnesium, phosphorus, and other essential minerals to combine with the calcium, our teeth and bones would not be as dense or hard and durable as they should be. Numerous studies have shown that, in regions where magnesium content is higher in water and food supplies, people have fewer bone fractures, less osteoporosis, and far less tooth decay."

"Is there really a chance that many of us actually suffer from magnesium deficiency?" the doctor asked.

"One of the most definitive studies ever made of this problem was reported in the *American Journal of Clinical Nutrition* by one of the foremost authorities on magnesium in the world, Dr. Mildred S. Seelig," I answered. "Dr. Seelig found that the American diet, on the average, is deficient by about 200 milligrams a day of the required amount of magnesium that most of us should be consuming for maintenance of good health. However, her study focused only on dietary deficiencies and didn't take into consideration other factors which tend to reduce further the amount of magnesium available to the body. One of these factors is stress, a malady all too prevalent in our modern world, which requires more magnesium as our body attempts to soothe and tranquilize frazzled nerves. Sugar in the diet also is antagonistic to magnesium, and we are painfully aware of the increase over the years in sugar consumption in this country. All in all, there are few people in this country who could not benefit from some magnesium supplementation in their diet."

My doctor looked at his watch and indicated that he was due back at his office for afternoon appointments. As we walked to the door of the restaurant, he turned to me and said, "You know, what you've told me about magnesium makes a lot of sense. I think I'll study more closely the idea of recommending chelated magnesium to some of my patients."

NOTES

1. H. Guthrie, *Introductory Nutrition* (St. Louis: C.V. Mosby Co., 1975, p. 141.)

ADDITIONAL READING

Feedstuffs, "Decline in Trace Minerals in Grain Shown," V. 41, August 9, 1969, p. 7.

Ashmead, D., "Hair analysis and the veterinarian," a paper given at the Minnesota Veterinary Medical meeting, Fairmont, June 1975.

Mulder, D., "Les elements mineurs en culture fruitiere," I Convegno Nazionale di Frutticoltura Montana d: Saint Vincent, 188, 1953.

Guthrie, H., *Introductory Nutrition* (St. Louis: C.V. Mosby), 1975.

Aikawa, J., *The Relationship of Magnesium to Disease in Domestic Animals and in Humans* (Springfield: Charles C Thomas), 1971.

Aikawa, J., *Magnesium: Its Biological Significance* (Boca Raton: CRC Press), 1981.

Jones, D., "Curing the nervous horse," *Horse and Horsemen*, 62, October 1978.

Ashmead, H., "Metabolic systems and their mineral activators," paper given at Miller Seminar for Physicians, Denver, December 1968.

Graff, D., *et al.*, "Absorption of minerals compared with chelates made from various protein sources into rat jejunal slices *in vitro*," a paper given to Utah Academy of Arts, Letters, and Sciences, Salt Lake City, 1970.

Seelig, M., "The requirement of magnesium by the normal adult," *Am. J. Clin. Nutr.*, 14:342, 1964.

15

The Roles of Chelated Magnesium and Other Minerals in a Healthy Heart and Arteries

The conference on nutrition and health was into its second day of lectures and workshops as we broke from a panel discussion for an afternoon recess. One of my colleagues met me at the back of the lecture hall to pursue a topic which we had only touched on in the previous panel discussion.

"I could tell from your comments today that you feel strongly about the need for augmenting our diets with mineral supplements," said my friend, inviting me to take a seat beside him. "What evidence do you have to support this position, given the fact that even a healthy body only maintains a relatively minute amount of minerals at any given time? It seems to me a waste to supplement the diet with minerals each day."

"Not at all," I replied. "There is good reason and much scientific evidence to support the need for mineral supplementation. In 1836, the Swedish chemist Berzelius discovered that small quantities of certain substances promoted chemical reactions and increased the rates at which these reactions occurred. He called these substances *catalysts* and found that they are needed in minute quantities in order to effect most chemical reactions. The catalysts themselves remain virtually unchanged as chemical reactions occur, allowing them to participate in a great number of these reactions before they lose their potency. In biology, where most of the chemical reactions are catalytic,

143

the catalysts wear out rapidly because the reactions can occur up to several million times per minute. Consequently, the catalysts must be replaced continuously."

"But what does all this have to do with the need for minerals?" asked my friend, with a puzzled look on his face.

"Other than for structural purposes such as for bones, minerals function mainly in the body as enzymatic catalysts in biological reactions," I replied, settling in for what promised to be a lengthy discussion.

"But according to my understanding of catalysts," my colleague added, "they cannot initiate a chemical reaction that otherwise would not occur. So even if the minerals aren't there, the reactions will still take place."

"I'd have to agree with you," I replied. "However, a vast number of vital chemical reactions are taking place in our bodies continuously, and virtually all of them are catalytic. In 1878, Kuhne recognized a certain type of catalyst in living matter, which he called enzymes.

"Enzymes govern and regulate the behavioral functioning of every living cell in our bodies. An ordinary cell can contain hundreds, sometimes thousands, of different enzymes which regulate the multitude of chemical activities that must take place if the cell is to live and reproduce itself. If all the enzymes were not there to accelerate the chemical reactions within the cell, it would probably die while waiting for the vital reactions to occur on their own, assuming that these reactions could occur on their own.

"A good example of the critical need for enzymes is in the heart cells. To pump blood throughout the body, the heart must expand and contract. As the blood fills the chamber, the heart expands. Then to force the blood out of the heart into the body, it contracts and squeezes out the blood."

"What you're telling me about the heart is common knowledge," said my friend, shuffling through some papers.

"You are right," I agreed, "but often things become so common that we fail to recognize their importance. The heart must maintain a certain amount of elasticity in order to expand and contract. The degree of elasticity in the heart depends upon a cell-manufactured compound called elastin. When an insufficient amount of elastin is produced by the enzyme lysyl oxidase within the heart cells, heart failure results. The heart is unable to pump blood if it can't stretch, so it quits working."

"That's interesting," my friend commented, "but it seems to me that we've gone a long way from the original question relating to the need for mineral supplementation."

"I'm glad you're keeping track of the conversation," I replied. "Actually, a discussion of enzymes and catalytic reactions relates directly to minerals because the greater part of the enzymes in our cells have a specific mineral attached to them which can be isolated from the enzyme. If the mineral is removed, the enzyme loses its activity, and when the mineral is replaced, the enzyme regains its catalytic properties. For example, copper is the mineral that activates the elastin-producing lysyl oxidase. When copper is deficient, the enzyme can't function and the elastin cannot mature. This results in lesions or enlarged hearts and ruptured arteries within the aorta and cardiovascular system.

"Keep in mind that all the cells in the body are in a dynamic state, with components being replaced continuously. There is a constant turnover of proteins and fats, together with a slower replacement of structures such as bones and tissues. Enzymes are subject to the same process of being constantly broken down and replaced, sometimes even before they are worn out. This process creates a continual need for raw materials such as amino acids to replace those used in the enzyme reactions. This need for raw materials extends to minerals, which the body may not always get even in a balanced diet. The resulting mineral deficiency could have a serious adverse effect on the efficiency of enzyme reactions within the body."

While my friend thought over the consequences of a general mineral deficiency, I tried to focus on a specific instance where mineral supplementation is necessary. "When someone undergoes open-heart surgery or has a heart attack, what is one of the first minerals you put into his body?"

"Potassium," he answered without hesitation.

"I agree. And this suggests that the body may be somewhat deficient in potassium since drastic supplementation is often required under such serious conditions. We know that most of the potassium in the heart is intracellular; that is, it exists inside the individual cells that make up the heart. We don't completely understand why potassium is necessary for the heart to contract normally and force the blood flow to the various parts of the body, but according to Dr. Helen Guthrie from Pennsylvania State University and Dr. Jerry Aikawa at the University of Colorado Medical Center enzymatic potassium is involved in activation of the nerves.

"When a specific nerve fires, the heart contracts and the blood is pumped out. Given a severe potassium deficiency, the heart will stop contracting altogether. In a potassium-deficient state, the heart muscle cannot relax and receive the returning blood. This condition creates additional work for the heart because it must pump harder to force returning blood back into the unrelaxed or contracted heart muscle. When this occurs, an individual's heart beats harder, and if the condition is severe enough, a heart attack can result.

"I remember several years ago when the liquid protein diet was popular. I wrote an article against this diet as practiced by most people. They were drinking water and a small amount of liquid protein. I predicted that unless people started supplementing their diets with other essential nutrients and in particular minerals, some of these dieters were going to have heart attacks. My message went unheeded until two people died. The autopsies revealed that they were severely potassium deficient and their hearts had quit working as a result."

"From what you're telling me," my friend said, "I can see that mineral deficiencies can certainly be a contributing factor in the rising incidence of heart problems."

"Besides the problems associated with potassium deficiency which I just described, you are most likely seeing other heart ailments which can be attributed to magnesium and phosphorus deficiencies."

"What do magnesium and phosphorus have to do with a healthy heart?" asked my friend, showing a new interest in our discussion.

"The heart cannot pump blood throughout the body without adequate energy. In each of the cells that make up the heart muscle, there is a small amount of a phosphorous-containing chemical called adenosine triphosphate, or ATP. When ATP is enzymatically broken down by the heart cells, energy is released to fuel the action of the heart. The enzyme required to break down ATP is called adenosine triphosphatase, but this enzyme is unable to function unless magnesium is pressent to activate it."

"I see what you're getting at now," my friend commented. "The heart is one muscle in the body that requires a great deal of energy to keep it working." I nodded in agreement as he continued. "The only way the heart can get the energy it needs is by utilizing that special enzyme to break down the ATP. However, the enzyme can't function properly if the body is deficient in magnesium because magnesium is the catalyst in the enzyme that allows it to break down the ATP.

"I've been led to believe that magnesium deficiencies are not that common," my friend continued. "Do you honestly think that magnesium deficiencies play a significant role in heart disease?"

This question did not have a simple answer, so I related my experience of a few years ago when I had visited a close business associate who had been rushed to the hospital a few hours earlier after suffering a heart attack. Even though he was still in the intensive care section of the hospital, I was allowed a short visit.

"Hello, John," I greeted in a subdued voice as I entered the room. I was intimidated by the profusion of monitoring equipment which seemed to entangle my friend as he lay in bed. "Considering what you have just gone through, you're looking pretty good," I told him, trying to sound optimistic.

Acknowledging my presence with a slight movement of his arm, my business associate said weakly, "Thanks for coming, DeWayne. When they first brought me in here I was afraid I wasn't going to see my friends or family again. I was scared of dying, and even the doctors and nurses seemed quite anxious and concerned."

"I'm sure you're in good hands," I encouraged him. "These doctors and nurses are some of the best at treating heart problems."

"They seemed to know what they were doing when they treated me," whispered my friend. "One of the first things the doctor ordered for me was an injection of magnesium. I distinctly remember him calling for an injection of magnesium."

As I stood in the dimly lit room watching the sophisticated monitors record every precious beat of my friend's heart, I felt reassured that the doctors treating him were aware and concerned about the importance of mineral nutrition relating to the heart.

Perhaps these doctors had read of a hospital study in which a team of physicians had observed almost three hundred patients who had been rushed to the hospital with acute heart attacks. Each had received exactly the same care when they arrived at the hospital except for one thing—half the patients were injected with magnesium upon admission to the hospital while the other half were not. During the next 48 hours, 20 percent of the patients who had not received the magnesium died, while only 7 percent of the injected patients died. From this study, it was shown that the magnesium injection following a heart attack could improve chances of survival by 16 percent.

I began to recall my own associations with this coworker over the past few weeks and tried to piece together the circumstances which might have led him to this life-threatening situation requiring substantial magnesium supplementation.

My friend had undertaken a major new project some weeks earlier, along with his usual office responsibilities. During that period, he had taken little time to relax or be with his family, since he was faced with a deadline for the completion of his project. He arrived at work early and returned home late and exhausted every night; after only a few hours of sleep, he would start the cycle again. The stress of the situation soon became apparent in his reduced energy level and loss of weight.

My associate's stressful condition became obvious to everyone at work as he became irritable and hard to please. At the slightest provocation, he would become angry with a subordinate and resort to irrational excuses for his own mistakes. On more than one occasion, I offered advice to my friend about his health, but the only thing that seemed to matter was the completion of his project.

About one week before the heart attack, my associate contracted a strain of flu which caused a high fever, excessive perspiring, diarrhea, and vomiting. He was finally forced to stay in bed for a few days. His condition led me to reflect on some medical research I had been studying which talked about the depletion of body nutrients during illness. Some studies have shown that diarrhea and vomiting can cause the body levels of magnesium to become dangerously low. Concern for my friend continued to grow as I heard more about his weakened condition.

Even though the man had not fully recovered from the flu, he returned to work after four days at home, saying, "Coming to work is better than lying at home worrying about it." I objected to his return while he was in such a weakened state, but his drive to complete his project outweighed his common sense.

Only a few hours after plunging back into his work, disaster struck. My associate clutched his chest as the pain intensified, and as he tried to stand up, he fell to the floor under the trauma of a heart attack.

As I sat by the hospital bed thinking about the factors leading to my friend's heart attack, I couldn't ignore the possibility of a severe magnesium deficiency.

Some days later, with my friend in a more stable condition, I visited again at his bedside. We discussed his improving condition as well as his brush with death a few days before. "Why do you think the doctors gave me a magnesium injection that first hour? What did that do for my heart?" he asked.

I briefly related what I had read in a British Medical Association publication, which reported that when a person experienced a heart attack, the chances of survival were generally one in three. After the introduction of magnesium injections, doctors found that only one in one hundred similar cases was fatal.

As I paused to reflect further on that statistic and the impact that it had had on my business associate, I was brought back to the present and the empty lecture hall as my doctor friend exclaimed, "That's a significant improvement when you think in terms of the number of lives saved each year. No wonder your business associate's doctor gave him magnesium."

I smiled with satisfaction at making my point. "Personally, I believe that most people would have much healthier hearts if they would adopt a regular mineral supplementation program to go along with proper rest, exercise, and other necessary dietary considerations. Minerals aren't the whole answer for a healthy heart, but they are certainly an integral part.

"Let me tell you," I continued, "about another research project in which Albion Laboratories was involved. Each person in this double-blind study suffered from diagnosed angina, a heart condition so painful that the person feels as if he is suffocating. Half the patients was given a targeted magnesium that had been chelated to amino acids in a special way so that more of the magnesium was directed to the heart; the other half were given a placebo. In the treated group only 50 milligrams of magnesium was given. That is considerably less than the RDA. At the end of two weeks the patients were subjected to a stress test, which caused their hearts to beat up to 160 beats per minute or until they suffered pain, whichever came first. They were each connected to cardiovascular devices, which monitored their systems during the test. Even after only two weeks on the magnesium supplements, this group was able to withstand significantly more stress and perform more physical work than it had been able to do before, while the control group showed no measurable change in performance. In fact, the ability to do physical work increased 25 percent with a corresponding decrease of 22 percent intake of nitroglycerine tablets in the treated group."

"I didn't realize that magnesium was so important to the heart," my friend commented. "I thought that potassium was the most common deficiency associated with heart attacks."

I understood my friend's concern since research has shown that when the fluid around the heart shows a low concentration of potassium, there is an outflux of potassium from within the cells in the heart muscle tissue. This depletion of potassium induces the sodium in the surrounding fluid to enter the heart cells in abnormal quantities. With the influx of extracellular sodium into the heart, increased arterial fibrillation occurs, which is spontaneous, very rapid beating of the heart.

Further, in congestive heart failure, doctors usually find high levels of sodium inside the heart cells. The potassium has left the heart and has been eliminated as body waste. If the patient in this condition (known as congestive heart failure) is to recover, the potassium must first re-enter the cells that compose the heart.

What I had told my friend about potassium was not new to him since potassium therapy has been a part of the normal therapy already in use with heart patients. He was more interested in returning to our discussion on magnesium.

"Magnesium and other minerals play an extremely important role in many cardiovascular diseases," I told him. "As you know, atherosclerosis means a hardening of the arteries. In this disease, lesions are formed in the large and medium-size arteries. Once these lesions have occurred in the walls of the arteries, the body deposits yellowish plaques containing calcium, cholesterol, and other fat materials. As the plaque deposits build up layer upon layer, the thickening of the arterial wall begins to impede the flow of blood through the arteries. If left unattended, atherosclerosis can be fatal because the blood cannot flow."

"I am seeing more and more problems relating to arteries,"

my colleague commented. "I know that surgery is a poor cure for atherosclerosis, but many times it's the only option when the arteries are so plugged up with the plaque. There must be another approach to the problem from a nutritionist's point of view."

"As you well know, the best cure is always prevention," I said. "Let's take a little closer look at how atherosclerosis begins, and then maybe we can understand more about how to prevent it. In the bloodstream, fat molecules are normally absorbed through the artery walls. If these artery tissues are damaged in any way or if the blood contains excess fat, then fatty streaks begin to appear on the interior walls of the arteries.

"In a symposium I attended on atherosclerosis, it was reported that whenever the arterial walls were injured, the damage localized and provided crevices in which fats were initially deposited. After being sufficiently anchored in the crevices, the fatty deposits were able to withstand the pressure from the flowing blood, thereby becoming more of a hindrance and threat to the proper flow of blood."

"Wouldn't one solution to the problem of fatty buildup around the lesions be to promote faster healing of the artery walls?" asked my friend.

"You're one step ahead of me," I smiled. "I'm certain that you are aware of the vital role played by zinc in the healing of body tissues. According to Dr. Walter J. Pories and others who work a great deal with zinc in their medical practices, when adequate zinc is present, a more rapid healing of the lesions reduces the chances for cholesterol deposits in the damaged artery. They have found that in many cases where body levels of zinc were supposedly normal, supplemental zinc still accelerated the healing process."

"Why do you suppose supplemental zinc was so effective?" questioned my friend.

"In the case of atherosclerosis, my own theory is based on a calcium-zinc relationship," I explained. "Remember that calcium aids in cementing or holding the fat deposits together as they build up on the arterial wall. In fact, frequently a calcium layer is deposited on the wall before the fat attaches itself. Calcium is antagonistic to zinc, and an excess of cellular calcium will push much of the zinc out of the cell. I have theorized that as the calcium is laid down in the injured area, some of it is absorbed by the cells in that area. This in turn pushes a portion of the cellular zinc out. The resulting zinc deficiency retards the healing process of the arterial wall, thus providing adequate time for permanent foundations of cholesterol to develop around damaged areas. Therefore, in my opinion, zinc supplementation is necessary to keep arterial walls healthy, particularly in view of the generally declining zinc values in the foods we are eating.

"Let's examine more closely the development of atherosclerosis after the foothold is established because of possible injury to the arterial wall and the subsequent localized zinc deficiency. As more fat and calcium are deposited around the nucleus beginning in the lesion, the arterial walls thicken and plaques of cholesterol, or fatty deposits, narrow the arteries. With a binding of these fatty deposits by the calcium, the arterial walls lose their elasticity and become hard and brittle. If a chunk of cholesterol breaks free from the wall or if a clot forms as the blood passes over a rough edge of plaque, the result could be a total blockage of the blood vessel."

"How do you relate these findings to our original discussion on magnesium?" asked my friend.

"Good question," I remarked. "The late Dr. Henry Schroeder along with several research associates reported in *The Journal of Chronic Disease* that when experimental animals were fed high-cholesterol diets and then given supplemental magnesium in their drinking water, the magnesium-containing waters protected them partially or completely against aortic atherosclerosis," I explained.

I referred to another research report I had recently read in *The Lancet*, a British medical magazine. "The researchers Bershon and Delsfse compared the cholesterol levels in the blood of native Africans to South African Europeans of similar age and sex. They found that in the newborn babies, cholesterol levels were the same for both groups, but as the individuals advanced in age the South African Europeans, who had consumed a different diet than the native Africans, developed an elevated level of blood cholesterol. The native Africans, showing normal or lowered cholesterol levels, also showed approximately 10 percent more magnesium in their bodies.

"After making several other magnesium studies, the investigators concluded that a definite correlation exists between the amount of magnesium and cholesterol in the blood. As magnesium is elevated, the cholesterol levels drop. These same researchers have shown that magnesium supplementation has a positive effect on atherosclerosis, although Dr. Pierre Delbert of the French Academy of Medicine has emphasized that magnesium should be considered as a food not as a drug.

"I think one key lies in an observation made by Dr. Lehman in *The British Medical Journal*," I continued. "He suggested that magnesium simply acts as an anticoagulant in the blood. This may be true since calcium is necessary for the blood to coagulate. In the absence of calcium, the blood fails to clot.

"Recently Albion Laboratories participated in a study on the role of magnesium in reducing coagulation. Human volunteers were given 180 milligrams of magnesium as an amino acid chelate, which was targeted to increase its absorption into the blood. After taking the magnesium supplement for seven days volunteers had a platelet adhesiveness that was reduced almost 40 percent. As you know, that reduction is significant when dealing with atherosclerosis."

"I'm beginning to see the picture," my friend interrupted enthusiastically. "Magnesium is antagonistic to calcium and, when supplemented in reasonable quantities, it will push excess calcium out of the blood."

"That's right," I agreed. "In an experiment in which I participated, we gave animals magnesium that had been chelated in a special way with amino acids. Some of the researchers at my laboratory analyzed the blood and blood serum for magnesium and calcium content at the beginning of the experiment and again thirty days later. They found that the magnesium levels had risen about 18 percent over the thirty days while, during the same period, the calcium had dropped about 5 percent in the whole blood and about 18 percent in the blood serum. Much of that excess calcium was either eliminated or metabolized by the body elsewhere; the important point is that the calcium left the bloodstream when subjected to the presence of the extra magnesium.

"With that calcium-magnesium relationship in mind, let's return to the problem of atherosclerosis. In my opinion, as the extra magnesium from metabolized supplements of magnesium reaches the bloodstream, because it is antagonistic to calcium, it has the tendency to remove from the blood the excess calcium that holds the fat deposits together. When enough calcium is removed from the plaques, they collapse and are reabsorbed by the body."

"You've built a strong case for mineral supplements," my friend remarked.

"Government findings, as well as research done by noted professionals all over the world, support the idea of supplementing one's diet with specific minerals, particularly as a person approaches middle age and enters the atherosclerosis age. But I wouldn't overlook mineral supplements even at an earlier age. U.S. government studies have shown that careful attention to a balanced diet, including mineral supplementation, can lessen the chances of being afflicted with atherosclerosis, and the earlier such a program is undertaken, the greater the success."

ADDITIONAL READING

Ashmead, H., "Trace minerals—There is a difference," paper given at the annual meeting of the National Health Federation, Salt Lake City, August 1973.

Schutte, K., *The Biology of the Trace Elements* (Philadelphia: J.B. Lippincott), 1964.

Gallagher, C., *Nutritional Factors and Enzymological Disturbances in Animals* (Philadelphia: J.B. Lippincott), 1964.

Guthrie, H., *Introductory Nutrition* (St. Louis: Times Mirror/Mosby College Publishing), 1986.

Aikawa, J., *The Relationship of Magnesium to Disease in Domestic Animals and in Humans* (Springfield: Charles C Thomas), 1971.

White, A., *et al.*, *Principals of Biochemistry* (New York: McGraw Hill Book Co.), 1973.

Cantin, M. and Seelig, M., eds., *Magnesium in Health and Disease* (New York: S.P. Medical and Scientific Books), 1980.

Nutrition Reviews, "Magnesium deficiency amd ischemic heart disease," 46:311, September, 1988.

Whang, R., ed., *Potassium: Its Biologic Significance* (Boca Raton: C.R.C. Press), 1983.

Pories, W., *et al.*, eds., *Clinical Application of Zinc Metabolism* (Springfield: Charles C Thomas), 1974.

Cramer, W., "Experimental production of kidney lesions by diet," *Lancet*, 223:174, 1932.

Schroeder, H., *et al.*, "Essential Metals in Man," *J. Chron. Dis.*, 21:815, 1969.

Burch, G., *et al.*, "The importance of magnesium deficiency in cardiovascular disease," *Am. Heart J.*, 94:649, 1977.

Weir, C., *Benefits from Human Nutrition Research: Human Nutrition Report No. 2* (Washington, DC: (US Department of Agriculture), 1978.

Ashmead, D., "Vital minerals and the liquid diet," *Bestways*, July 1979.

Manganese
A Brief Introduction

M anganese has been found to be an essential body nutrient because of its integral role in a variety of biochemical reactions within the body. The greatest concentrations of this mineral are found in the pancreas, liver, pituitary gland, and kidneys. Manganese is an important catalyst and a cofactor or component of many enzymes in the body.

Manganese is also necessary for normal skeletal and connective tissue development. Few elements have as many metabolic functions, although the mechanisms promoting these functions are obscure. Some of these functions include (1) proper utilization of glucose, (2) normal pancreas function and development, (3) prevention of sterility, (4) cholesterol synthesis, and (5) lipid synthesis and metabolism.

Although no RDA has been established for manganese, the National Research Council estimates that if infants obtain between 0.5 to 1 mg per day of manganese, if children obtain between 1 and 2 mg of manganese each day, and adolescents and adults between 2 and 5 mg each day, they are within a safe level. Incidents of manganese toxicity are relatively uncommon, however.

Acute manganese deficiencies in human beings are not common. Nevertheless, symptoms of a deficiency may include a weakness of ligaments and tendons, ataxia (muscular incoordination), possible diabetes, myasthenia gravis and multiple sclerosis, dizziness, convulsions, and glandular disorders. Based

157

on these and other symptoms, a manganese deficiency may prove to be more common than heretofore thought.

16

Manganese: Are We Overlooking Its Importance?

I n most instances when I am involved in discussions relating to mineral nutrition, I take the posture of the lecturer or teacher. However, I am continually learning and understanding more of the intricacies of human nutrition brought to light by the research of others on the subject. Such was the case some time ago when I approached a university professor for some advice about a research project on which I was working.

"Often in our attempts to understand how a certain nutrient functions in the body, we tend to oversimplify what is happening," commented the professor. "The functions of most nutrients are multifaceted, which make their roles complex. To isolate one role or action is extremely difficult."

As the professor continued to explain, I was becoming frustrated because what I had envisioned as a simple research project was growing much more complicated than I had anticipated.

"Beriberi," the professor said, "which we now know is caused by a deficiency of vitamin B_1, or thiamine, was first recognized by the Chinese as early as 2600 B.C. By 1855, Japanese sailors were obtaining relief from the disease by changing their diets from what was usually supplied by the navy to include vegetables, meat, and fish. In 1890, a Dutch scientist discovered a cure for beriberi—unhusked rice or rice polishings. Nevertheless, it wasn't until 1926 that thiamine was identified and extracted from the rice hull. Finally, in

159

1936, thiamine was successfully synthesized, and by 1961, thiamine production worldwide was over 200 tons."

I showed some impatience with his history lesson by commenting, "But what has that got to do with our discussion of manganese?"

The professor smiled tolerantly as if I were one of his students, then continued. "In 1939, synthesized thiamine was still new, and many researchers were studying it. A scientist by the name of Peria, working with two other scientists named Sandberg and Holly, discovered a synergistic effect between vitamin B_1 and manganese. In fact, these researchers concluded that the thiamine requirements of the body may depend to an extent upon the amount of manganese in the diet. They recommended taking manganese supplements to improve the utilization of vitamin B_1. Later testing confirmed their findings."

I knew vitamin B_1, or thiamine, to be essential in the body's utilization or metabolizing of carbohydrates and fats, as well as for the production of glucose in all body cells. I was also aware that thiamine is needed for protein synthesis and for the transmission of nerve impulses at the nerve synapse. In fact, the absence of thiamine in the enzymes regulating these processes leads to a slowing or a complete blocking of the chemical changes in the body. However, the professor's statement about thiamine and manganese was something about which I wanted more information.

"What does the manganese have to do with vitamin B_1 utilization?" I asked.

"Remember the synergistic relationship I mentioned earlier?" questioned the professor. "This relationship involves several enzymes which act as catalysts to energize the thiamine through phosphorylation. One of the enzymes with which I am familiar is thiaminokinase. Manganese is necessary to activate that enzyme. When we ingest thiamine, it is not in an active form and so must be converted by the body to a viable substance. The enzyme thiaminokinase, activated by manganese, takes the vitamin and adds to it an energy molecule called adenosine triphosphate, or ATP. The resulting chemical reaction produces thiamine pyrophosphate, the active form of thiamine. Thiamine pyrophosphate is then capable of serving as a cofactor in the enzymatic reactions that metabolize carbohydrates and perhaps other essential nutrients.

"You see," he added, "this active form of thiamine is needed to maintain a normal appetite and to aid in digestion and the normal functioning of the nerves and heart. The testicles in the male also require this active form of vitamin B_1. All these uses are in addition to the carbohydrate metabolism for body energy which I mentioned earlier. However, without the mineral manganese to activate the thiaminokinase enzyme, none of these chemical reactions will take place. We may call the results of that deficiency a vitamin deficiency, but it can really be better classified as a shortage of the mineral manganese.

"We know that manganese is also present in the enzymes that synthesize complex carbohydrates and mucopolysaccharides within the body cells," the professor continued. "Thus manganese appears to have more than one role to play in supplying the body with energy."

"Based on what you're telling me about the relationship between manganese and thiamine," I said, "the American public is probably wasting a great deal of money on this B vitamin."

"Why is that?" the professor asked.

"For inorganic manganese from a soluble salt to be absorbed, it must first be chelated, that is, chemically bonded in a certain way to amino acids in the intestine or to carrier proteins on the surface of the intestinal cell. The mineral can then be moved across the cell towards the blood by a special group of amino acids that make up a specific manganese carrier-protein called transmanganin. In other words, for manganese to be absorbed, it must follow an intestinal absorption pathway similar to that of iron. Like iron absorption, manganese absorption can be as low as 1 percent of the total amount of the dietary intake, depending on the source of the mineral and the foods that are in the digestive tract when the manganese is trying to be absorbed.

"Although the federal government has not set daily requirements for manganese even though it has established both a need and safety levels, Briggs and Calloway, in their book *Nutrition and Physical Fitness*, estimate that the human adult male needs between 6 and 8 milligrams of manganese per day compared to the 3 to 5 milligrams required by adult females. It worries me to think that the body is dependent upon at least that amount of manganese every day when you consider that it takes approximately 1.75 ounces of manganese-rich foods such as nuts, whole-grain cereals, dried legumes, or tea to supply just 1 milligram of manganese. When you realize that only a certain percentage of the manganese in those manganese-rich foods will be absorbed and put to use by the body, the possibility of deficiencies is great."

"I'm afraid I can't agree with you," argued the professor. "No one has ever reported a manganese deficiency among humans."

"In absolute terms, that's probably true," I agreed. "But have we really seen the deficiency for what it is or have we covered it up by calling it some other type of problem? Furthermore, what about marginal deficiencies? Carbohydrate metabolism could be affected by low levels of manganese. We wouldn't recognize that as a manganese deficiency. It would come across as a problem in energy production. What about a biological interference with certain sexual functions? We might call that an emotional problem and recommend psychiatric treatment when in reality it could be a manifestation of a nutritional deficiency. An entire new discipline is emerging in psychiatry called orthomolecular psychiatry. This approach to the treatment of emotional or mental disorders is based on nutrition rather than on the traditional remedies offered in psychiatry. Pfeiffer, *et al.*, recommend using manganese and zinc in the treatment of schizophrenia. They have found high levels of iron and copper in the schizophrenic and use zinc and manganese to remove them. Pfeiffer also recommends that certain amino acids be used in a chelate in order to target the manganese and zinc to the brain.

"Research further suggests that a manganese deficiency may be responsible, in part, for the degeneration of discs between vertebra in the back. In fact, a doctor and I published the results of a research project in a medical journal in which we showed that when a manganese deficiency in the body was detected (based on previously developed norms), there was a tendency for the discs that cushion the vertebra to degenerate. When high levels of manganese were given to experimental animals suffering from this disease, their discs repaired themselves and the backs of the animals returned to normal, as evidenced by X rays. In addition, viral infections may gain a foothold in the body if there is insufficient manganese to help create cellular barriers against the viruses."

"If what you are saying is true," added the professor, "why have I never seen a case of manganese deficiency?"

"Perhaps you have seen evidence of manganese deficiency without recognizing it," I responded. "I have seen some interesting laboratory test results which show mineral levels in thousands of people. One striking statistic from these observations is that there is a reduced level of manganese in persons who were later diagnosed as cancer patients. In fact, manganese levels in cancer patients were found to average 50 percent lower than manganese levels of healthy subjects."

"Do you mean to tell me that manganese deficiencies cause cancer?" responded the professor.

"I didn't say that," I replied. "But consider some facts. Manganese is essential for synthesis of glycoproteins in the cells of the body. As you know, glycoproteins are amino acid chains which have sugars hooked to their sides. Those sugar molecules cannot be attached to the protein without the presence of two enzymes called glucosyltransferase and galactosyltransferase. However, before either of these enzymes can function, chelated manganese must be present to activate them. If there is a manganese deficiency in the body, the enzymes won't work, and the sugars are not attached to the amino acid chains. If the sugars are not attached, then there is no synthesis of glycoproteins."

"What is so important about these glycoproteins?" asked the professor.

"Glycoproteins form part of the membrane on the surfaces of the billions of cells in the body," I answered. "Although they comprise only a minor part of the total cell membrane, glycoproteins are important because they appear to be responsible for protecting the cell from invading viruses. Recent research showed that the cell surfaces of cancerous cells do not have the same glycoprotein coating as normal cells.

"As late as 1973, researchers discovered that interferon is a glycoprotein. Interferon is probably a natural antiviral agent produced by the body. However, as with other glycoproteins, it can probably be produced only when there is adequate manganese in the body to activate the necessary enzymes."

"What you are saying," injected the professor, "is that low manganese levels in the body may allow a cancer virus to attack the body cells because the body cannot build up its natural defense without the manganese to help synthesize the defending glycoproteins."

"That is very possible," I replied.

"What is the answer, then, to low levels of manganese?" questioned the professor. "The amount of food that may have to be eaten to produce a satisfactory body level of manganese makes the solution impractical for many."

"Taking small molecular weight manganese supplements which are properly chelated with amino acids so that the chelate is stable and will survive the stomach acids and the enzymes in the gastrointestinal tract seems the most logical solution for many," I replied. "In research conducted by Albion Laboratories, it was found that the process of manufacturing the manganese chelate was extremely important if the metabolism of the manganese was to be maximized. When the chelate was buffered correctly, body utilization was 250 percent greater than if an equal quantity of an improperly made chelate was ingested. More manganese of the proper kind was absorbed through the intestine, and stored in the liver, kidney, and bones. At the same time, an additional amount was discovered in certain body tissues requiring manganese."

The professor smiled at my enthusiasm for the subject of mineral nutrition as he added, "As I remember, you came to me today to ask for some advice on how to proceed in your research. As usual, you've turned it into a learning experience for me."

ADDITIONAL READING

Guthrie, H., *Introductory Nutrition* (St. Louis: Times Mirror/Mosby College Publishing), 1985.

White, A., *et al.*, *Principles of Biochemistry* (New York: McGraw-Hill Book Co.), 1973.

Schramn, J. and Wedler, F., eds., *Manganese in Metabolism and Enzyme Function* (Orlando: Academic Press), 1986.

Ashmead, H.D., *et al.*, *Intestinal Absorption of Metal Ions and Chelates* (Springfield: Charles C Thomas), 1985.

Briggs, G. and Calloway, D., *Nutrition and Physical Fitness* (Philadelphia: W.B. Saunders Co.), 1979.

Pfeiffer, C., *et al.*, "Blood histamine, basophil' counts, and trace elements in the schizophrenias" in Hawkins, D. and Pauling, L.. eds., *Orthomolecular Psychiatry* (San Francisco: W.H. Freeman and Co.), 463 – 512, 1973.

Pfeiffer, C., *Mental and Elemental Nutrients* (New Canaan: Keats Publishing, Inc.), 1975.

Nipko, R. and Ashmead, D., "The cause and prevention of canine disc disease," *Vet. Medicine/Small Animal Clinic.*,72:337, 1977.

Ashmead, D. and Beck, B., "Chelated minerals and cancer," paper given at the annual meeting of Cancer Victims and Friends, Los Angeles, 1978.

17

Minerals and the Back

The second day of the conference on nutrition was coming to a close as many of the participants gathered for dinner in the hotel dining room. As I looked for a place to sit, I saw a familiar face across the room and walked excitedly toward an old friend.

"Charles," I exclaimed, as the friend rose to greet me. "I expected to see you yesterday at the opening of the conference."

"I expected to be here," said my friend, a prominent medical researcher. "However, I had other work, which kept me away until this evening. What has been keeping you busy since we talked last?"

I explained to him that I had recently returned from a medical convention in Boston, where I had submitted a year's worth of research data to the editor of a medical journal. "I have been working on a project with a veterinarian friend," I continued. "He is convinced that the findings of our research will have a major impact on veterinary medicine."

"It sounds exciting," responded the doctor. "What does your research involve?"

"One of the most common and most aggravating medical problems known to man," I replied, smiling at the puzzled look spreading across his face. "We've been doing research on the relationship of minerals to back problems."

"I hadn't realized that you were so interested in veterinary medicine," said my friend, motioning to the waiter that we were ready to order our dinner.

167

"Actually," I responded, glancing quickly at the menu in front of me, "I believe that the information we have gained from our research on the vertebra of dogs will be invaluable as research on the treatment of human patients progresses because dogs have many of the same types of back problems that humans do, such as degenerating and ruptured discs."

After the waiter had taken our orders, I continued. "As you know, the discs in the back act like shock absorbers or cushions between each vertebra. Often the discs harden and are no longer able to absorb the shock waves that are produced when the back moves. Hardened discs have a tendency to rupture, forcing some of the disc material against the spinal cord. The resulting pressure against the nerves in the spinal cord is the cause of many acute back and leg pains and, if severe enough, can even cause paralysis. As the problems of this sort develop in dogs, the veterinarian usually resorts to surgery on the back."

"When these same problems arise in human beings," my doctor friend responded, "the patient is faced with three solutions. First, the person can be treated by a chiropractor. This type of treatment is usually effective only when the deterioration of the discs is not too pronounced. Second, the person can be treated with drugs. This solution deals mainly with the symptom by attempting to mask the pain and rarely has any real effect on the cause of the problem. Third, the patient can submit to surgery, a choice often made at the sacrifice of future flexibility and proper functioning of the back."

"I would hesitate to call these options solutions," I said, "because at best these remedies are only temporary. The drugs and surgery options are generally available to the dog, too, but our research has indicated that a high percentage of the animals undergoing drug therapy or surgery were never able to resume full, unrestricted activity."

"That is also true of many of the people I treat with back problems," replied the doctor. "But at this point, I have no other reliable method of dealing with chronic back problems. Do you?"

"I believe I do," I answered. "In a study conducted by Dr. Priester, he reported that after he and thirteen colleagues had reviewed 8,117 case histories involving people with disc problems, the doctors concluded that generally the cause centered around inadequate nutrition to the disc material."

"What type of nutrition was missing?" he asked.

In answer to his question, I took some of my research papers from my briefcase and spread them out on the table. I explained that in chemical analysis done by our laboratory of normal discs and discs taken from dogs who had back problems, we found that there was 61 percent less iron and 91 percent less manganese in the discs of dogs with degenerative conditions.

I could tell that I had caught my friend's interest with my research statistics, as he responded, "I'm sure you have read many publications on nutrition which claim that a deficiency of manganese is unknown or at least not measurable. You've just suggested to me that these tests may be wrong and that manganese deficiencies are at the root of many back problems."

"I have read a large percentage of those reports about manganese," I said. "I would have to agree that manganese, unlike calcium or phosphorus, exists in the body in only trace amounts. In fact, the whole body of an adult human only contains between 12 and 20 milligrams of manganese. That's less than one hundred-thousandth of an ounce. Thus, it is difficult to measure a body deficiency of manganese. Nevertheless, in a five-book treatise on mineral metabolism, Professors Comar and Bronner reported that slight changes in the mineral composition of the body cells—changes that are so small that only the most sophisticated scientific equipment can measure them—will result in profound metabolic disturbances in the body. In spite of these metabolic disturbances, the clinician would generally not find a recognizable deficiency of manganese."

"But how do those small changes affect the back?" my doctor friend asked. "I've read that slipped tendons in poultry are a result of a manganese deficiency. Does that relate to the problems with the back in dogs and in humans?"

"Let me explain," I said, ignoring the plate of food the waiter set in front of me. "In the body, both chelated iron and chelated manganese are involved in the production of collagen, the material which makes up the disc. As you know, in spite of its minute quantities in the body, manganese is an essential catalyst for the proper functioning of many enzymes as either a cofactor or as part of the enzyme itself. If the manganese is absent, the enzyme won't work. For example, manganese is needed to synthesize the carbohydrates and fats in the body. Without manganese, glucose cannot be utilized in the production of collagen. Furthermore, the polymerase enzyme that actually builds collagen must have manganese in order to make the disc material.

"Under normal circumstances, the disc material is continually being destroyed and replaced by new collagen. In order for the body to manufacture new collagen for the discs, adequate amounts of iron and manganese, as well as vitamin C, must be present. These minerals and vitamin work together to enable the body to assemble all of the ingredients which make up the disc collagen. [See Figure 17-1.] If there is a deficiency of these nutrients, the production of new disc material is hampered, usually resulting in degeneration and rupturing of discs."

The doctor finished a bite of food and then added, "This indicates to me that perhaps proper nutrition may prevent a great number of these back problems. But what about patients that are already afflicted with disc problems?"

"That's the exciting part of our research," I answered. "During the study, we gave nutritional supplements of specially chelated minerals and vitamins to fifty-four completely and partially paralyzed dogs which were candidates for surgery. Since laboratory assays had shown that manganese was the most seriously deficient mineral, we gave the dogs extra manganese that had been specially chelated with amino acids. During that year, every dog whose nutrition was changed to include these supplements regained complete use of its limbs. The X rays taken by the veterinarian helping to conduct the research confirmed that with the added vitamin and mineral

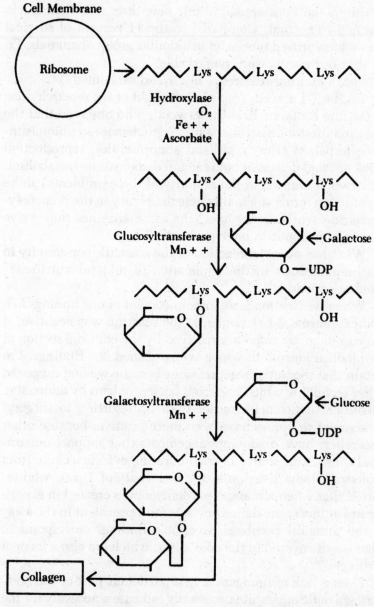

Figure 17 – 1. Processes in the production of collagen. Source: R. Nipko and D. Ashmead, "Canine Disc Disease," *Veterinary Medicine/Small Animal Clinician*, 72:1339, 1977.

nutrition, the dogs actually built new discs and their backs returned to normal. Compared to the 11 percent of surgical cases which proved successful in a similar group of animals, I'd say that our results were remarkable."

"That's exciting research," my friend exclaimed.

"Yes it is," I agreed, "especially in light of the research done by the late Professor Eric Underwood, who observed that the main manifestations of manganese deficiencies in animals include impaired growth, skeletal abnormalities, reproduction problems, and defects in both fat and carbohydrate metabolism. Underwood found that the majority of these problems can be explained in terms of a manganese deficiency in the mucopolysaccharide synthesis enzymes, the same enzymes that we've been talking about in back problems."

"What has been the reaction of the scientific community to this breakthrough in the application of mineral nutrition?" asked my friend.

"When we first made an announcement of our findings in a medical journal," I responded, "the reaction was negative, if you can judge by responses received by the editorial section of the medical journal in which we published our findings. I'm certain that the initial reaction came because we had suggested a new technique which corrected back problems by addressing nutritional deficiencies rather than by resorting to surgery. Subsequent responses have been more positive, because other researchers have made announcements that support our original thesis. One source of corroborating evidence came from Professor Gladys Everson at the University of Texas, who reported that when a manganese deficiency is created in experimental animals, the deficiency was most prevalent in the assay of the animals' cartilage. Everson's findings correspond to what we discovered in the dogs' discs, which are also a form of cartilage."

"Does a lack of manganese in a particular part of the body during a deficiency state necessarily indicate a necessity for the mineral?" questioned my friend.

"I'm sure that question was raised by Dr. Everson," I responded. "That's probably why she and her associates went on to prove that the manganese was absolutely essential for the normal development of cartilage. Further, Dr. James Lassiter at the University of Georgia reported at an international symposium that he was convinced that a manganese deficiency was a basic cause of joint disease. Other independent researchers have reported similar findings, so in the end, in spite of the initial skepticism, it appears that the veterinarian and I will be proven correct in our findings about the importance of manganese."

"I can see that you have been well occupied in the time since we talked last," remarked my friend as we finished our dinner. "If it takes this long before I see you again, you're likely to have discovered a cure for the common cold."

"Oh, I'm working on that one," I chuckled as we rose to leave. "Don't be surprised if the answer to that one has to do with minerals also."

ADDITIONAL READING

Nipko, R. and Ashmead, D., "Canine disc disease: Cause, prevention, and a new approach to treatment," *Vet. Med./Small Animal Clinic.*, 72:1337, 1977.

Comar, C. and Bronner, F., *eds.*, *Mineral Metabolism* (New York: Academic Press), V. 2, 1964.

Underwood, E., *Trace Elements in Human and Animal Nutrition* (New York: Academic Press), 170 – 195, 1977.

Hoekstra, W., *et al.*, *Trace Element Metabolism in Animals—2* (Baltimore: University Park Press), 1974.

Everson, G., "The effects of manganese deficiency during gestation of the offspring," in Mills, C., ed., *Trace Element Metabolism in Animals* (Edinburgh: E.S. Livingstone), 125, 1970.

Phosphorus
A Brief Introduction

Phosphorus has more functions than any other essential mineral in the body. Most recognizable is its role as a major constituent of bones and teeth. Because phosphorus is often discussed in connection with calcium, its function in the formation of hard tissues tends to overshadow the valuable role that phosphorus plays in other parts of the body.

Phosphorus compounds play a central role in energy transformations, whether that energy is derived from fats, carbohydrates, or proteins. The nucleoproteins responsible for the process of cell division, reproduction, and the transmission of hereditary characteristics are dependent upon phosphorus as an integral part of their molecular structures. All cells in the body contain some phosphorus in the form of phospholipids.

An excessive consumption of sugar seriously upsets the calcium-phosphorus balance necessary for normal body functioning. It has been postulated that the reason the polio virus, which thrives in an atmosphere of calcium-phosphorus imbalance, historically flourished in the summer was due in part to the increased consumption of soft drinks, with their high concentration of sugars. Many carbonated beverages also contain substantial phosphorus (up to 500 mg per serving), adding to the problem of calcium-phosphorus imbalance.

The recommended dietary allowances (RDA) for phosphorus as established by the National Research Council are 240 mg for infants, 360 mg for infants from six months to one year of age,

800 mg for children one to ten years, 1200 mg for males and females twelve to eighteen years, and 800 mg for males and females over the age of eighteen. During pregnancy and lactation the daily intake of phosphorus should be increased by 400 mg.

Deficiency symptoms of phosphorus may include poor bone and tooth structure, arthritis, pyorrhea, and rickets. There can be mental and physical fatigue and nervous disorders. Irregular breathing, appetite loss and weight loss, or even obesity may also accompany a phosphorus deficiency.

18

Phosphorus
More Than a Companion for Calcium

As the dentist made his final marks on my checkup chart, the dental assistant adjusted the chair to a more upright position and removed the cloth napkin from around my neck.

"I'm just making a note on your chart to watch an old filling on one of your lower molars," he said. "Otherwise, your mouth is in pretty good shape. You must be exercising it regularly," he joked.

"If you're referring to my lecturing," I responded, "I've been keeping pretty busy lately on the convention circuit. How is your family doing?"

"Well, my twins just turned eleven," he said with noticeable pride. "They seem to be asserting themselves in different directions all of a sudden. For the first ten years, you could hardly tell the two girls apart, both in appearance and in emotional makeup. If you talked about one, you had to mention the other in the same breath. Lately, however, Jenny is becoming quite an athlete, while Jody is developing her homemaking skills like cooking and stitchery. They've become independent, although they still rely on one another quite a bit for support."

"Doctor," I interrupted excitedly, "you've just given me an idea for one of my upcoming lectures on mineral nutrition. I'm certain you didn't intend it, but let me explain."

"You mean you're going to relate my twins' development to mineral nutrition?" questioned the dentist.

"In a way," I replied. "As you were describing your girls

177

and how you could hardly mention one without thinking of the other, I thought of how nutritionists have generally paired two of the major minerals found in the body, calcium and phosphorus."

"That's only natural," said the dentist, "since both are required to build strong teeth and bones. Don't the two minerals always work together?"

"Just as your twins seem to be finding their own identities," I explained, "calcium and phosphorus are being separated by many nutritionists, because research is revealing their many independent and essential functions in addition to their combined roles in forming bones and teeth."

"I have a reference book that I use on nutritional questions," interjected the dentist, turning to his bookshelf. "Let's see what Helen Guthrie has to say about your subject in her book *Introductory Nutrition.*"

"An excellent choice," I replied, reaching for the book. I flipped a few pages and then read:

> The role of phosphorus as a major constituent of bones and teeth is recognized by even the casual student of nutrition. The fact that it is often discussed in connection with calcium has further emphasized its role in the formation of hard tissues, with the result that its other equally vital roles are often overlooked or underestimated.
>
> It is estimated that the adult body contains 12 gm. of phosphorus per kilogram of fat-free tissue. This amounts to about 670 gm. of phosphorus in the male and 630 gm. in the female. Of this phosphorus, 85% to 90% is in the form of the insoluble calcium phosphate (apatite) crystals that give rigidity and strength to bones and teeth. The remaining 10% to 15% is distributed throughout all living cells of the body, with about half present in striated muscle. Specifically, phosphorus is a part of the nucleus and the cytoplasm of every living cell, where it not only plays an essential role in many body processes but also serves as a structural component. In fact, practically all biological reactions involve phosphorus to some extent, since it is vital to any reaction that involves the uptake or release of energy.[1]

"It sounds like a very interesting subject," my friend acknowledged, putting away the book and taking a seat on the stool in front of me. "What else can you tell me about the lesser-known functions of phosphorus in the body?"

"I can probably tell you more than you want to know right now about phosphorus," I said, trying not to seem too eager at his invitation.

"On the contrary," reprimanded my dentist. "You are my last patient today, and I'm always interested in discussing nutrition with you. In fact, much is being written lately in some of the journals I read about the correlation between balanced nutrition and healthy teeth and gums. So let me have it; what does a mineral expert like yourself have to say on the subject?"

"You mentioned the role of phosphorus in the development of bones and teeth," I began, "but I think we need to clarify how phosphorus is involved in these two different parts of the body. Once a tooth has been formed, there is very little turnover of the minerals which make up its structure. The teeth are not like bones, which are constantly being dissolved and replaced with new calcium and phosphorus."

"Are you saying that once a person's teeth are developed, he or she doesn't need much phosphorus to keep them healthy?" inquired my friend.

"Not exactly," I continued. "According to the National Institute of Technology, tooth decay is frequently the result of a mineral deficiency rather than a bacterial disease. We all show evidence of the same bacteria in our mouths, yet some of us experience tooth decay while others don't. Apparently it is not so much what we eat as what we do not eat that determines whether or not the bacteria in the mouth will cause the teeth to begin decaying. One of the critical nutrients affecting this particular bacteria is phosphorus."

"What did the research show?" asked the dentist, eager to hear more.

"I remember reading Dr. Charles Bronsen's report on the subject," I offered, "and he said that although phosphates are not recognized as bactericides, in adequate concentration in saliva they appear capable of inactivating those acid-agenic bacteria found in the mouth, probably through a change in the pH of the mouth. This disclosure that with adequate levels of phosphorus in the saliva phosphates could be produced to inactivate pathogenic bacteria may reverse present medical concepts regarding the natural means which the body uses for inactivating certain other pathological bacteria in the system besides dental caries. According to Dr. Bronsen, phosphorus could be the most potent systemic antibiotic known.

"I remember a few years ago writing an article on phosphorus which was published in a popular nutrition magazine. One of the readers became upset by my article because I subscribed to the premise that many people suffer from phosphorus deficiencies even though their phosphorus intake is adequate. This reader stated that when he corrected his calcium-to-phosphorus ratio in the blood, his saliva became alkaline and his dental problems disappeared. He attributed the alkaline saliva to calcium. I suspect he thought of calcium as an alkaline earth metal and phosphorus as a phosphoric acid. What he overlooked was that phosphorus exists in the body primarily as a phosphate, which is also alkaline. The important point, however, is not that he may have attributed his alkaline saliva to the incorrect mineral, but that the alkaline saliva resulted in a significant reduction of dental problems."

"I understand your point," replied the dentist. "I remember that when the saliva is alkaline, an amylase enzyme becomes active and could help digest bacteria, which are primarily responsible for tooth decay," he coaxed, leaning forward on his stool.

"During a research project conducted by Albion Laboratories, we found a pattern in mineral levels among persons who developed more than two cavities each year. This pattern was significantly different from the mineral levels shown in persons who developed less than two cavities per year. [See Table 18-1.]

"As you know," I continued, "scientists have shown a definite relationship between the amounts of calcium, magnesium, and phosphorus in the body. High body levels of calcium or mag-

Table 18-1.   Comparison of Mean Levels of Calcium,
Magnesium and Phosphorus
of Two Groups of Dental Patients.

	Saliva	Urine	Hair
Calcium:			
Less than two restorations	7.85	15.49	119.0
More than two restorations	9.11	9.16	101.45
Magnesium:			
Less than two restorations	1.01	12.28	13.74
More than two restorations	1.37	11.35	7.3
Phosphorus:			
Less than two restorations	.259	.950	—
More than two restorations	.201	.969	—

Ca and Mg levels are reported in Mg%. P levels are reported in Mg/ml.

nesium will depress the absorption and metabolism of phosphorus and vice versa. In our study, which was conducted in cooperation with several dentists, we found that the group who had two or more dental cavities per year had higher than normal calcium and magnesium levels in their bodies. Phosphorus levels were lower than normal, particularly in the saliva. The phosphorus was presumably lower because of the presence of high amounts of these other minerals."

"What makes you so sure it was the calcium and magnesium that caused the deficiency of phosphorus?" asked the dentist.

"Because this research was not designed to measure that particular parameter, I can't be absolutely positive," I admitted. "But let me tell you about another study in which we were involved. Under the supervision of a physician, adult volunteers were given either twice the RDA of magnesium or 1.5 times the RDA of calcium in the form of amino acid chelates. In both cases, the amount of phosphorus in the body was decreased as a result of those minerals being ingested. Based on that research, I would suppose that we are seeing the same type of picture in the dental experiment."

"So Albion Laboratories showed by their research that less phosphorus in the saliva relates directly to more tooth decay in the patient," concluded the dentist.

"Yes," I responded. "And we discovered that only about 10 percent of the people we tested had adequate phosphorus levels in their saliva as reflected by one cavity or fewer. Most of the people falling into the adequate group had no tooth decay at all over a given one-year period."

"Are you implying that most people suffer from some degree of phosphorus deficiency?" questioned the dentist.

"I'm sure that most nutritionists wouldn't complain about the phosphorus content of the average American diet," I said. "But I doubt seriously whether adequate amounts of phosphorus are actually metabolized by most people. Its bioavailability may be questionable."

"What do you mean, exactly?" asked the dentist.

"Let me explain it in this way," I continued. "About 80 percent of the phosphorus in the body is combined with calcium and found in the bones and teeth. The actual structuring of the bones and teeth is due to a protein matrix, which holds the minerals together in a crystalline form. The remaining 20 percent of the phosphorus in the body is also in combination with proteins, lipids, and carbohydrates. This complexed phosphorus can be found in our blood, muscles, and every other living cell within the body. In each of these instances, phosphorus functions in the body only after it undergoes a process called phosphorylation."

"What's that?" asked the dentist.

"Phosphorylation is the process of attaching the phosphorus compound into an organic carrier substance, such as the amino acids found in the body," I explained.

"Do you mean that the phosphorus is chelated?" my friend asked.

"No," I answered, "the phosphorus is complexed. When the body chelates a mineral, it chemically suspends that mineral ion between amino acids in such a way as to form ring structures. The chemical structure of phosphorus is such that, unlike most minerals, it behaves as a carrier of amino acids and is classified as an anion in the phosphate form. Because of these properties, phosphorus cannot form a ring structure with the amino acids but can only be attached to them.

"What this means to your body," I continued, "is that ingested phosphorus will attach itself to various substances along the digestive tract, but only that portion which attaches to the amino acids will be absorbed properly. In an international seminar on calcium and phosphorus held in Vienna, Austria, in 1981, it was reported that in order for inorganic phosphorus to be absorbed through the intestine into the blood, it required the presence of vitamin D to attach the phosphorus molecule to a carrier protein. Thus, the absorption of phosphorus is vitamin D dependent and is controlled by certain hormones. Conceivably then, regardless of intake from dietary sources, the body levels of phosphorus could be low due to extenuating factors outside the quantity of phosphorus intake. As you may know, some of our research at Albion Laboratories has shown that when phosphorus is complexed with amino acids in a specific way before ingestion so as to make it compatible with the body, absorption and metabolism of the mineral increases dramatically. This was shown in an Albion study supervised by a physician in which adult volunteers were given 1.3 grams of phosphorus as an amino acid complex for ninety days."

"So adequate body levels of phosphorus don't necessarily come with just a balanced diet," added the dentist, "because absorption can be affected by so many variables."

"That's a point I try to make in my lectures," I said. "Deficiencies are far more common than the average person realizes. According to the Nutrition Foundation, vitamin D deficiencies, liver disease, some drugs including antacids, and other factors can cause phosphorus deficiencies. And without adequate phosphorus in the body, the proper functioning of every cell is jeopardized because phosphorus controls the pH of the body, transfers energy, and functions in numerous other activities in the body, including the formation of bones and teeth."

"I'd like to hear your next lecture," said the dentist, "especially if you'll be comparing your mineral relationships to my twins."

"You know that you're always welcome wherever I speak," I said, getting up to leave, "and bring the twins along."

NOTES

1. H. Guthrie, *Introductory Nutrition*, St. Louis: C.V. Mosby Co., 1975, p. 131.

ADDITIONAL READING

Guthrie, H., *Introductory Nutrition* (St. Louis: C.V. Mosby Co.), 1975.

Ashmead, H., "Nutrition and dental health," paper given at the annual convention of International Association of Oral Myology, Denver, June 1980.

Ashmead, D., *et al.*, "Mineral analysis of hair as related to metabolic disorders," paper presented to Southern California Academy of Nutritional Research, Los Angeles, October 1974.

Bronsen, C., "Land and Food," *Applied Trophology*, 17:7, 2nd quarter, 1974.

Bronner, F. and Peterlik, M., eds., *Calcium and Phosphate Transport Across Biomembranes* (New York: Academic Press), 1981.

White, A., *et al.*, *Principles of Biochemistry* (New York: McGraw Hill Book Co.), 1973.

Odden, C., *et al.*, "Mineral metabolism and interactions in human beings," unpublished research paper, 1976.

Harrison, H., "Phosphorus" in Nutrition Foundation, *Present Knowledge in Nutrition* (Washington, DC: The Nutrition Foundation), 241 – 246, 1976.

Potassium
A Brief Introduction

P otassium is found mostly within the cells of the body instead of in the extracellular fluid surrounding the cells. Although potassium is ignored by many as a nutrient, the daily requirement for an adult is approximately 2,500 mg, more than twice that of calcium or phosphorus. One probable reason for the lack of emphasis on potassium is the fact that it is widely distributed in many of our most common foods and the daily requirement is not difficult to achieve. Because of this, the National Research Council has not established recommended dietary allowances (RDA) for potassium. Nevertheless, supplements for adults should not contain more than 99 mg of potassium. A tablet, capsule, or liquid supplying 100 mg or more potassium is considered to be a drug and is treated as such by the Food and Drug Administration.

Potassium plays a major role in maintaining the osmotic pressure of the cell. It is also a factor in the transmission of nerve impulses and in the release of insulin from the pancreas.

The use of diuretics and cortisones, or conditions like diarrhea, vomiting, severe trauma, diabetes, renal disease, and excessive sodium chloride (table salt) intake could lead to a negative potassium balance in the body. Symptoms of a deficiency may include edema (swelling), thirst, constipation, dry skin, general muscular weakness and impairment of neuromuscular functions, slow or irregular heartbeat, and nervous disorders including insomnia and poor reflexes.

185

19

Potassium
A Natural Guardian Against Heart Attacks

Not long ago, a close friend of mine went to a heart specialist after experiencing some irregularities in his heartbeat. After a thorough checkup, the doctor prescribed digitalis, a heart-regulating drug, which my friend took for several weeks with no noticeable improvement. The doctor then increased the dosage and gave my friend quinidine, another heart-regulating drug. Shortly after taking the increased dosage and additional drug, my friend began suffering from severe headaches and nausea. He continued to take the drugs under the doctor's care for another week, when his vision began to blur. When I noticed that he had begun wearing glasses to correct his vision, I asked what the problem was.

My friend related the details of his condition and told me what the doctor had prescribed. I suggested that he talk to his doctor about a possible toxic reaction to the drugs, which he did at his next visit. At first the physician refused to accept toxicity as a reason for the problems my friend was suffering from, so at the request of my friend, I agreed to contact the doctor myself.

After a brief discussion with the physician about my friend's condition, I mentioned the possibility of a toxic reaction to the medication. The physician refused again to accept toxicity as a possibility, but upon my insistence, he finally conceded that it was possible. "But," he added, "that size dosage shouldn't cause toxic reactions."

"I realize that the dosage is a normal one and generally

188 *Conversations on Chelation and Mineral Nutrition*

would not cause toxicity," I agreed. "but did you think to check the patient's potassium level before prescribing the medications?"

"That's not part of our normal routine in dealing with minor heart problems," admitted the doctor.

Noticing a book on the doctor's shelf with which I was acquainted, I took the liberty of using it to substantiate my position. The book was the *Physician's Desk Reference,* and I quickly turned to a section on potassium levels in the body. "It says here," I read, "that a potassium deficiency in the body or an imbalance of potassium to sodium sensitizes the body and particularly the heart to toxicities of cardiovascular drugs, even at lower doses. A suggested counter measure for the situation is potassium supplementation."[1]

Following this meeting with the doctor, he put my friend on potassium supplements. Within a week or two, many of the side effects of the heart-regulating drugs began to vanish even though the dosages remained the same. However, my friend's vision has never returned to what it was before he began taking the drugs. He related to me that as long as he takes the potassium the drugs seem to work fine, even at decreased dosages, and he even thinks that some day in the future he may be able to do without the heart-regulating drugs altogether.

In one of our many conversations since his heart troubles, my friend asked me to explain something. "How, exactly, does potassium work in the heart?"

"Well," I responded, "all of its biological functions are not yet completely understood. As far as the heart is concerned, most of its potassium supply is inside the millions of individual cells that make up the heart. However, there is also a low concentration of potassium in the fluids that bathe the heart muscle; the potassium is needed for the heart to contract and force blood out to the various parts of the body. In its absence, the heartbeat can be irregular."

"My doctor always used that term, irregular," responded my friend. 'What did he mean when he said my heartbeat had some irregularities in it?"

"For one thing," I answered, "the velocity with which the

blood is pushed out of the heart into the arteries is increased. The speed of the blood rushing from the veins back into the receiving chamber of the heart is also accelerated. You feel this change as rapid and hard beating of your heart. In some cases, when it becomes severe enough, it may precipitate the early stages of a heart attack. If left uncorrected, the potassium deficiency could cause returning blood to be blocked altogether from entering the heart, which means that the heart would be stopped from beating. Keep in mind, however, that this is only one type of heart attack and not necessarily a frequent one."

"Are there other heart problems that can result from a potassium deficiency?" my friend pressed.

"Research has shown that when there is a potassium deficiency in the body, one of the first places this deficiency is recognizable is in the fluids bathing the heart. In such a condition, the high concentration of sodium, which is also found in this fluid, has nothing to keep it in check. In the normal heart fluid, the sodium and potassium are in balance, but with the potassium deficiency in the fluid, the sodium starts to enter the individual cells in the heart muscle. When this happens, the sodium forces the potassium out of the heart cells into the fluid. This ultimately creates a potassium deficiency inside the heart cells themselves.

"At this point," I continued, "the physician will start seeing irregularities in the heartbeat. The potassium has left the heart and been eliminated in the urine. Congestive heart failure generally results. If the patient ever recovers from the congestive heart failure, the potassium must first re-enter the cells that compose the heart."

"How difficult is it to replace potassium lost in this manner?" questioned my friend. "Are supplements effective?"

"That depends a lot on the nature and composition of the supplement," I said. "With all the different products available, a doctor has to know what will work best for his patient. To illustrate this point, let me tell you about a cousin who underwent open heart surgery to replace valves in his heart some time ago.

"After a successful operation to repair a rather delicate and life-threatening heart condition, my cousin was recovering in the hospital. Because the body loses potassium during most illnesses and particularly in postoperative states, the doctor had included a potassium supplement in my cousin's IV. The doctor was simply replacing the potassium the man had lost by injecting it directly into the veins.

"The man's recovery seemed to be progressing quite well, so after a couple of weeks or so, he was allowed to go home to continue his recovery in his own bed. A few days later, however, he was rushed back to the hospital. In the emergency room the doctors found that he was retaining fluids which had diffused from the bloodstream through the walls of the blood vessels into the extracellular fluid compartments of the body, particularly around the heart. That condition allowed more sodium to accumulate in the fluids, which in turn was reducing the potassium levels. The high sodium levels were also replacing the potassium within the heart cells, and my cousin experienced congestive heart failure."

"So because he was taken off the intravenous potassium supplement, his potassium level dropped too low," observed my friend.

"That's right," I answered. "Fortunately, the doctors were able to save him. He spent several more weeks in the hospital, during which time the doctors gave him diuretics, that is, drugs that remove fluids from the body. Unfortunately, the diuretics also cause sodium retention within the body. Potassium supplements including potassium gluconate were prescribed, but none of them seemed to be effective in raising his overall potassium level. Finally, the doctor agreed to try a form of potassium that had been complexed with amino acids, which my cousin had obtained on his own.

"For the first time since my cousin had undergone surgery months earlier, he started absorbing and retaining enough potassium to keep him free from danger of further damage to his heart. His blood level rose to 3.7 milliequivalents per liter of potassium. At first the doctor couldn't believe what he was seeing. He took my cousin off the potassium and put him on a different kind. The blood potassium level dropped to 2.5

milliequivalents per liter of potassium. When he resumed the supplementing of the amino acid complexed potassium, the body potassium level rose to the normal level and stayed there. His physical condition improved rapidly, and the doctor was so astounded by the results that he wrote up the case history for a medical journal."

"Why was the amino acid complexed potassium absorbed so much better?" asked my friend.

"Researchers have learned that much of the potassium found naturally in the body is complexed to amino acids before, during, and after absorption. This is the way the mineral functions in the body. If we complex the potassium properly with amino acids before ingestion, apparently absorption and metabolism are both enhanced."

"The body is a complex system," I continued, "and only certain forms of minerals can be used. If the potassium is not complexed as the body would do it, then the body must rearrange the molecular structure of the complex in order to metabolize it. During this rearranging process, some of the mineral may be lost to the body and never used."

"I thought that the process you're talking about was called chelation," observed my friend. "Isn't that what most of your research has been focused on?"

"You're right about my research," I agreed, "but there is a fundamental difference between minerals which are chelated and those which can only be complexed.

"Visualize an atom of a mineral as being like a miniature solar system. The nucleus, like the sun, is in the center and the electrons, like the planets, revolve around the nucleus. The difference is that there can be more than one electron in an orbit, which is called a shell. Each shell can contain a certain number of electrons. When that shell is full with the specified number of electrons, then the addition of another electron starts a new shell. In a stable atom the electrons, each of which has a negative charge, equal the number of positive protons in the nucleus. In that case the atom is stable and not reactive."

"I appreciate your course in chemistry," my friend interrupted, "but what does that have to do with potassium?"

"I was just getting to that," I continued. "If the electron is removed from the outer shell, or orbit, the atom becomes unstable because it has more positive charges than negative ones. Thus it wants to join with a negatively charged atom or molecule in order to become electrically neutral. In the case of a mineral which is chelated, at least two electrons are removed from the outer shell. Thus when it is chelated to an amino acid, one end of the amino acid will share its electron with the mineral, and the other end will curve around and also be bonded so that a ring structure results. The mineral ion bonds the two ends of the amino acid to make the ring.

"In a complex, only one electron is in the outer shell and that is all that can be removed. Thus the potassium can have a + 1 charge, but no more. It can be bound to one end of the amino acid but not to the other. It forms a straight chain amino acid complex, but not a ring-structured chelate." [See Figure 19-1.]

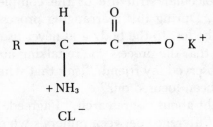

Figure 19 – 1. **Potassium Amino Acid Complex.**

"In other words," responded my friend, "if I see a potassium product on the market which claims to be chelated, I'll know that the manufacturer hasn't done his homework."

"That's right," I replied. "If you don't complex potassium with amino acids to increase its bioavailability, you may as well do nothing to it because the body will have to make the necessary modifications for inorganic potassium salts that are ingested."

"With the heart problems I've had in the last few years,"

said my friend, "I don't think I would be willing to take a chance on providing my body with needed potassium by taking a supplement that was not complexed."

NOTES

1. D. Huff, ed., *Physician's Desk Reference* (Oradell: Medical Economics Co., 1983, p. 1119.

ADDITIONAL READING

Huff, B., eds., *et al.*, *Physicians' Desk Reference* (Oradell: Medical Economics Co., Inc.), 1983.
Soffer, A.J., *Potassium Therapy* (Springfield: Charles C Thomas), 1968.
Whang, R., ed., *Potassium: Its Biologic Significance* (Boca Raton: C.R.C. Press, Inc.), 1983.
Goodhart, R. and Shils, M., eds., *Modern Nutrition in Health and Disease* (Philadelphia: Lea & Febiger), 1980.
Harper, H., *Review of Physiological Chemistry* (Los Altos: Lange Medical Publications), 1971.
Ashmead, H.D., *et al.*, *Intestinal Absorption of Metal Ions and Chelates* (Springfield: Charles C Thomas), 1985.

Selenium
A Brief Introduction

As a relative newcomer to the trace mineral arena, selenium has only recently been accepted as an essential nutrient to the human body. Its major function is that of an antioxidant in the enzyme glutathione peroxidase, and, in that regard, selenium appears to be as much as 100 times more potent than vitamin E. Also, a deficiency of this mineral increases many fold the body's need for vitamin E.

It is now evident that selenium plays a role in preventing degenerative changes in the pancreas. At low levels, it can also exert a protective effect in retarding growth of cancer tissue.

The National Research Council has not as yet established a recommended dietary allowance for selenium. Nevertheless, based on data derived from animal research, the council currently believes that the maximum intake of this element should not exceed 200 micrograms (mcg) per day for adults.

20

Selenium
The Two-Edged Sword

T here are few minerals that have undergone as dramatic a metamorphosis as selenium. For years it was regarded as toxic and therefore dangerous. Marco Polo, in the journal of his travels, wrote that he had observed "a poisonous plant . . . which if eaten by [horses] has the effect of causing the hoofs of the animals to drop off." Most researchers now believe he was observing a selenium toxicity because excessive amounts of selenium will cause lameness and hoof abnormalities in horses.

Similar symptomology was observed by others throughout the ensuing decades. In an 1860 report from Fort Randall in Nebraska, a U.S. Army surgeon, Dr. T.C. Madison, described the same clinical signs of a selenium toxicity in horses as did Marco Polo. He termed the problem an alkali disease.

Finally in 1934, the Department of Agriculture established that selenium was the toxic element causing these diseases. On a molar basis, selenium was and still is considered one of the most toxic of all elements, even exceeding arsenic. From this 1934 discovery until the middle 1960s, most investigators recommended avoidance of the mineral even though there was some evidence of a biological role in poultry as early as 1941. No formal work was done on the need for selenium in human beings until the 1960s.

Selenium is a two-edged sword. Taken in excess through environmental exposure, food and water contamination, or over-supplementation, it will cause loss of hair and nails and increases

197

in dental caries. In extreme conditions actual loss of teeth has also been noted. Dr. Carl Pfeiffer has reported that too much selenium will cause dermatitis (a disease where the skin becomes inflamed), lassitude, and progressive paralysis.

When acute poisoning has occurred the person develops a fever of between 103° and 105°F. This is followed by an increased respiratory rate. Next comes gastric upset and inflammation of the spinal cord and bone marrow. This leads to extreme weakness, terminating with death.

It is little wonder that the late Professor Eric Underwood, one of the foremost authorities on mineral nutrition, wrote in the 1956 edition of *Trace Elements in Human and Animal Nutrition*, "Interest in selenium as a trace element is almost entirely confined to its toxic properties . . . ." By 1962, in the second edition of the same book, Dr. Underwood had revised his opinion. He wrote that selenium's role as an essential element had only just become apparent. And in 1977, he wrote that selenium is necessary for growth, fertility, and the prevention of various disease conditions.

This new research is what causes selenium to be a two-edged sword. Taken in excess, the toxic manifestations previously outlined may result. On the other hand, if it is eliminated from the diet, the consequences can be equally devastating. Selenium has several important beneficial effects on the body if, according to Carl Pfeiffer in his book *Mental and Elemental Nutrients*, the daily intake does not exceed 200 parts per billion (ppb). This is the same amount recommended by the National Research Council—200 micrograms per day.

Selenium protects the body against the toxic effects of cadmium. In this role selenium functions as a scavenger and complexes the heavy metal. When the cadmium is bound to the selenium, it is no longer able to enter into the biological reactions which produce detrimental effects in the body. As a pollutant, cadmium seems to concentrate in the sex organs of both males and females, resulting in hemorrhaging and killing of the tissues, and, in the case of pregnancy, toxemia to the mother and death to the fetus. Research by Parizek and his coworkers at the Czechoslovakia Academy of Science in

Prague demonstrated that selenium supplements prevented the effects of cadmium in the male gonads and the ovaries.

Nonreproductive poisonous effects of cadmium, such as hypertension, were also prevented with selenium. In experimental animals that were intentionally overdosed with cadmium, the survival rate was much greater in those animals that received selenium supplements.

These same researchers reported that selenium has a similar effect on mercury poisoning, which we can get from contaminated seafood. For example, they found when lethal doses of mercury were ingested supplements of selenium completely protected the kidneys or intestine and insured survival. However, this was due to redistribution of the mercury into other organs rather than rapid urinary excretion. Once selenium had redistributed the mercury, it was slowly expelled from the body in the normal fashion.

It should be pointed out that both mercury and cadmium have a similar detoxifying effect on selenium. When a person ingests high amounts of either mercury or cadmium, these metals will drive selenium out of the body, resulting in a potential selenium deficiency. Dr. O. Levander of the Human Nutrition Research division of the U.S. Department of Agriculture (USDA) has reported that arsenic has a similar effect on selenium.

Dr. Pfeiffer has reported that in human beings selenium increases the effectiveness of vitamin E. Vitamin E appears to function in biological systems as a fat-soluble antioxidant. It is believed that selenium is converted into one or more organic compounds in the body which have the same antioxidant properties as vitamin E. These two nutrients may function synergistically or independently. More research will be needed to elucidate selenium's true role as an antioxidant.

It is known that in a vitamin E deficient state the body does not utilize selenium as effectively. According to Dr. Levander of the USDA, vitamin E increases the availability of the methyl groups from the amino acid methionine, which then combine with the selenium for several biochemical reactions in the body.

There appears to be a synergistic effect between selenium and vitamin E as far as the absorption of that vitamin is concerned. In experimental work done with selenium, it was shown that when a diet is deficient in selenium, vitamin E levels in the tissue are also depressed. In other work it was shown that intestinal absorption of vitamin E as well as other fats is limited when a selenium deficiency exists. From this research it appears that selenium functions in the absorption of dietary vitamin E.

There is a possible relationship between selenium and cancer. As early as 1943 Nelson, *et al.* published an article in the journal *Cancer Research* (3:230), in which they reported that high dietary intake of the mineral appeared to be carcinogenic. Russian investigators confirmed these findings in 1963 when they fed 10 parts per million of selenium to test animals. Other researchers have also suggested that high intake of selenium can produce or contribute to liver cancer.

But again, selenium is a two-edged sword. In 1949, Clayton and Baumann reported in *Cancer Research* (9:575) that selenium taken in lower amounts could also prevent cancer. This observation has also been confirmed by other investigators. For example, in 1966, it was shown that ingestion of 5 parts per million of selenium—half of what was reported to have caused cancer in an earlier study—would reduce the incidence of that disease. In fact one researcher, R. Shamberger, has published several studies which demonstrate that selenium can inhibit cancer in human beings. And Professor Underwood has written that selenium, far from being the carcinogenic agent that some of the early experiments had appeared to suggest, could actually be an anticancer agent.

Dr. Carl Pfeiffer believes that in functioning as an antioxidant selenium prevents chromosome breakage. If a chromosome within a cell is damaged, this affects the cell's ability to control its rate and form of multiplication. When body cell multiplication rates get out of control, cancer may result. Dr. Pfeiffer has noted that there are studies in which the cancer rate is unusually high when selenium intake is low.

In research done at a university using selenium as part of an experimental antioxidant agent, Albion discovered that cancer in laboratory animals was arrested and in many cases reversed. That does not suggest that Albion Laboratories has found a cure for cancer, but the research does tend to substantiate the theory that at least some forms of cancer can be controlled by removing the oxidizing free radicals from the body.

Without any doubt we need selenium in our diets. A deficiency may result in irreversible or life-threatening conditions if left untreated. Males appear to need more selenium than females. The exact requirements are unknown. Consequently, we should probably be cautious in taking supplements that contain large amounts of selenium. In small amounts it is essential for life, but in large doses selenium is more toxic than arsenic.

Good natural sources of selenium are brewer's yeast, garlic, liver, and eggs. Usually more selenium is obtained from animal sources than from vegetable sources. Consequently vegetarians who do not consume eggs may wish to supplement their diets with commercially prepared selenium supplements if clinical tests determine they are low in that mineral.

I hesitate to wholeheartedly endorse taking preparations high in selenium without medical supervision. At present there is meager evidence on the direct effects of selenium supplementation on humans. Most of our research has been done with animals because selenium can be so toxic. In a report issued by the National Academy of Sciences in Washington, DC, it was found that selenium toxicity in humans more frequently resulted from dietary excess than for any other reason.

ADDITIONAL READING

Pfeiffer, C., *Mental and Elemental Nutrients* (New Canaan: Keats Publishing, Inc.), 1975.

Underwood, E., *Trace Elements in Human and Animal Nutrition* (New York: Academic Press), 302 – 346, 1977.

Levander, O., *et al.*, "Characterization of the selenium in rat liver mitochondria as glutathione peroxidase," *Biochem. Biophys. Res. Commun.*, 58:1047, 1974.

Nelson, A., *et al.*, "Liver tumors following cirrhosis caused by selenium in rats," *Cancer Res.*, 3:230, 1943.

Clayton, C. and Baumann, C., "Diet and Azo Dye tumors: Effect of diet during a period when the Dye is not fed," *Cancer Res.*, 9:575, 1949.

National Academy of Sciences, *Recommended Dietary Allowances* (Washington, D.C.: National Academy of Sciences), 162–163, 1980.

Passwater, R., *Selenium As Food and Medicine* (Washington, D.C.: National Academy Press), 1983.

National Research Council, *Selenium in Nutrition* (Washington, D.C.: National Academy Press) 1983.

Diplock, A., "Trace Elements in Human Health with Special Reference to Selenium," *Am. J. Clin. Nutr.*, 45:1313. 1987.

Zinc
A Brief Introduction

Z inc is second only to iron in the ranking of trace mineral levels in the body. Much has been learned about zinc recently; zinc is emerging as essential for good health. It has been suggested by many that zinc deficiencies are as widespread among Americans as are those of iron.

Zinc is a constituent of over twenty-five enzymes involved in digestion and metabolism and is also essential in synthesis of nucleic acids, which relates it to growth, and regeneration of new tissues. Zinc is necessary for the absorption and activity of vitamins, particularly those in the B-complex group. Zinc is an essential element in all aspects of the reproductive process and is also necessary for normal prostate function. Although it is not part of the actual insulin molecule, zinc is a key component in the function of insulin in the body. Zinc has also been closely linked with the healing of wounds. Recent studies have shown that zinc concentrates in wounded tissues and plays a role in incorporating cystine into the protein of the skin and the conversion of glycine and proline into skin collagen. With measured doses of zinc in either topical or oral applications, healing time can be greatly reduced.

The National Research Council's recommended dietary allowance (RDA) for zinc is 3 mg per day for infants up to six months, 5 mg for infants six months to one year, 15 mg for children one year to six years, 10 mg for children seven years to ten years, and 15 mg per day for all males and females over ten years of age. In pregnant women the intake should be increased by 5 mg, and in lactating women the increase should be 10 mg.

If an individual is deficient in zinc the symptoms of that deficiency include: increased fatigue, decreased alertness, susceptibility to infection, slow wound healing, prostatitis, sterility, slow sexual maturity, retarded growth, loss of taste and smell sensitivity, and possibly diabetes.

21

Zinc Is Necessary for Life Itself

R ecently I met with my publisher to discuss an idea for a
book on mineral nutrition. We discussed the importance
of good health in general, and I explained to him my interest
in educating people about the necessity of balanced mineral
nutrition. As we talked about these needs, my friend seeméd
particularly interested in the importance of zinc as it relates to
human nutrition.

"Why is zinc so important?" he wanted to know.

"Working with magnesium and phosphorus, one of the
most important functions of zinc is its role in the production of
body protein," I explained. "You see, protein is not stored in
the body the same way fats and sugars, such as glycogen, are
stored. When we eat protein, it is digested, and what is not used
in growth and maintenance of body tissue is immediately used
for energy. Digested and metabolized protein is first used to
make new protein for the building of new cells in the body,
but the rest is used for energy, so it isn't stored.

"As you know, the body is made up of trillions of cells. Each
cell is a single living entity which attempts to live in harmony
with all other cells of the body. In an adult human, millions of
cells are daily dying and constantly need to be replaced by new
cells. The replacement of worn-out cells is accomplished by
cellular division, which occurs when a cell matures and divides
into two identical cells. These two daughter cells, as they are
called, in turn mature and divide, resulting in four cells.
When we reach adulthood, this cellular division normally

happens at a rate which approximates the death of older cells, thus allowing the adult body to maintain a status quo.

"Each cell in the body contains a small amount of a chemical called deoxyribonucleic acid, or DNA. If we could see the DNA molecule under a microscope, we would see it as a double strand that twists much like a spiral staircase. The basic elements of the long molecule are held together by phosphorus. Because of its unique structure, DNA becomes a blueprint containing all the information and instructions necessary for the cell to reproduce itself. As the cells do this, we see the activity as body growth and development through the creation of these new cells. Since DNA is present in all our body cells, it also plays a key role in telling each cell what its specialized activities are. Because of DNA, heart cells always become heart cells and liver cells always become liver cells."

"What does all of this have to do with zinc?" interrupted my friend.

"Well," I replied, "DNA has the ability to synthesize itself within each cell, but zinc, along with several other minerals, are required to activate numerous enzymes that help put the DNA together. If the cell is zinc deficient, then new DNA cannot be produced. When DNA synthesis stops or slows down, the number of new liver cells, brain cells, or other cells that can be produced is limited. Therefore, if the body is severely deficient in zinc, DNA production is hampered. With a deficiency of DNA, the cells in the body cannot reproduce themselves, and the ultimate result is death. A complete absence of DNA or zinc is probably impossible for a living organism, but if either is severely deficient, the consequences can be devastating.

"If this condition arises in a younger person, growth can be retarded. For example, Dr. Ananda Prasad described several cases in Iran where a zinc deficiency in the diet had resulted in dwarfism. The individuals he described all ranged in age from eighteen to twenty-one years, yet none of them was even 5 feet tall. They had no pubic hair and suffered from hypogonadism, which means that their sex organs were very small and not developed properly for their age.

"I realize that if we are already mature adults, we aren't really concerned about growth, but in the adult body, a vast number of other medical problems may manifest themselves besides growth. These include anemia, an inadequate immune system, mental retardation, sexual dysfunction, and sterility. All these conditions stem from the body's inability to grow new organ and tissue cells to replace the millions of cells that are continuously wearing out and dying. The National Research Council, which sets the standards for nutrient requirements in the United States, advises that zinc deficiencies in pregnant women can result in malformed babies and/or behavioral disturbances in children."

"It sounds as if life itself is fairly dependent upon the body maintaining an adequate supply of zinc," added the publisher.

"You're absolutely right," I responded. "It's just too bad that more emphasis hasn't been placed on zinc research over the years to help determine the extent of our dependence on it. In fact, zinc has only been recognized as an essential nutrient to the human body since the early 1960s. It is now believed that zinc deficiencies are relatively widespread throughout the world, including some areas of the United States. The National Research Council has stated that there are areas in the United States where zinc supplementation is recommended because a certain percentage of the population is consuming a zinc-deficient diet.

"I am beginning to understand what you are saying about the importance of zinc and the consequences of not getting enough of this mineral in the diet," said my friend. "Was Dr. Prasad able to determine why the dwarfs you mentioned earlier were not getting enough zinc in their diet?"

"According to the reports I've read, Dr. Prasad found that the people in the study principally subsisted on a grain diet. Grains generally contain large amounts of phytic acid, which will tie up zinc in the diet if it is there and make it unavailable to the body. Since grains are typically low in zinc anyway, in my opinion, the dwarfs' heavy intake of phytic acid was probably tying up any zinc ingested from other sources. Dr. Prasad's discoveries eventually became the starting point of the zinc interest that is now gripping nutritionists.

"Agricultural scientists, however, had a head start on the problem of zinc deficiencies. They had known for years that many farmlands were beginning to manifest zinc deficiencies. As early as 1927, zinc fertilizers had been found to be beneficial to Florida vegetable crops."

Referring to the book *Recommended Dietary Allowances* published by the National Academy of Sciences, I quoted, "There are wide areas in the United States where the soil is deficient in available zinc and where the appearance of spontaneous zinc deficiency in farm animals has necessitated zinc enrichment of foods."[1]

"In another study," I added, opening a folder of papers, researchers at West Virginia University found that low zinc levels appear in sweet corn when the soil in which the plants are grown is treated with artificial fertilizers heavy in phosphorus and nitrogen. Their finding is significant and could provide the best clue as to why zinc levels in various plants and foods have seen a steady decline. The heavy application by farmers of yield-boosting chemical fertilizers may be putting great strains on the soil's slender reserves of zinc and results in zinc-deficient foods."

"Zinc deficiency sounds like a serious problem," added my publisher, "but I don't recall any major outbreaks of dwarfism in this country. Are there some more common manifestations of zinc deficiency?"

"We could talk about several problems, including dermatitis acne and other skin problems, slow healing from surgery, loss of taste, loss of appetite, and poor growth in children," I responded, "but let me give you one example that is directly related to alcohol consumption. Many researchers believe that a zinc deficiency may be one of the main causes of cirrhosis of the liver. Studies have shown that when even moderate amounts of alcohol are ingested, there is an immediate decrease in the amount of zinc present in the liver.

"Alcoholic cirrhosis of the liver is caused by excessive consumption of alcohol and is characterized by the progressive destruction of liver cells. The destruction of liver cells is accompanied by the generation of a different type of liver tissue containing increased connective tissue, which we see as a hardening of the liver."

"Does that mean that the new, harder tissue is produced without the benefit of sufficient zinc?" asked my friend.

"Zinc is one mineral in particular that is affected by alcohol," I continued. "Studies have shown that alcohol causes changes in the body's ability to metabolize zinc. Even though sufficient quantities of zinc may be ingested from the diet, because of the presence of alcohol, the body tends to excrete much higher than normal levels of zinc, resulting in a possible zinc deficiency. There are probably other factors involved in cirrhosis of the liver, but many researchers believe that a lack of sufficient zinc adds significantly to the deteriorating effect of alcohol on the liver."

"I'm certainly no expert on health matters myself," my publisher added, "but I've read recent articles linking zinc with many types of preventative and curative remedies."

"However," I continued, "the value of zinc can hardly be limited to the maintenance of a healthy liver. Zinc is also essential for the formation of new bone. Extensive studies made by the Veterans Administration and reported by Dr. Noah Calhoun have found that a deficiency of zinc will greatly retard the process of bone regeneration."

"So maybe if I break my leg," my publisher said, "I should take some extra zinc to help my bones mend faster."

"You'd be surprised at the positive results gained from just such applications of zinc supplements," I responded. "Of course, we don't go around breaking bones every day, but unknown to many of us, our bones are engaged in a continual process of dissolving old bones and returning their mineral components into the bloodstream; at the same time, new bone is being produced as replacement, and these two processes must be kept in balance. A lack of zinc will retard the formation of new bone cells (the precursor to actual bone formation) while not affecting the breakdown of the old. This imbalance can easily result in the development of a bone condition called osteoporosis, an all-too-common condition in which the bone, instead of being solid and dense, develops little holes like a sponge that cannot be filled in."

"Is zinc a major component of the bones?" questioned my friend.

"That's a good point," I answered. "In order to keep the bones well mineralized and solid, zinc is certainly not enough. What we chiefly need is calcium and phosphorus and a number of other minerals such as magnesium and manganese. However, if we lack sufficient zinc, these other minerals will not help to keep the bones strong.

"Most people don't realize the need for these minerals in bone formation. I remember an examination I took for certification as a nutritionist. The question related to the need for specific components for bone formation. I knew I was supposed to say that calcium and phosphorus were essential. Instead I talked about zinc. The examiner was unfamiliar with the research I quoted and disallowed my answer. I only got it accepted when I appealed.

"One might well suppose that zinc's importance goes back to its role as an essential element in the formation of DNA. As I said before, DNA contains the instructions or blueprint that each cell must follow in reproducing itself. Without DNA there can be no cell reproduction, and if the instructions themselves are somehow reproduced defectively because of the deficiency of zinc, then the attempts of the cell to reproduce itself will also be defective."

"If what you say is true," interrupted my publisher, "a zinc deficiency could adversely affect the health of the body in a thousand different ways."

"Let me give you some support for that conclusion," I added, looking through some more papers. "Dr. Walter Pories, in an address to the American Association for the Advancement of Science, said: 'Investigators have demonstrated in rapid succession that zinc deficiency is common in man and that this deficiency is a critical factor in impaired growth, delayed healing, and chronic disease.'[2]

"Since that announcement," I continued, "a number of studies have emphasized even more sharply how difficult it is for people to get enough usable zinc in their diets despite the desperate need for sufficient zinc to maintain good health and reproductive capabilities."

"What do you mean by reproductive capabilities?" asked my friend.

I explained to him that zinc is involved in the production and function of several sex hormones. "To give you an example," I said, "severe zinc deficiency has been shown to cause male sterility. In research at Albion Laboratories, we have been successful in identifying zinc-deficiency-caused sterility in animals and in correcting it through supplementing their diets with a zinc that has been chelated in a special way so that the mineral is carried specifically to the sex organs. Through this targeting of zinc, many sterility problems have been overcome.

"Not only can sterility result from inadequate dietary zinc," I added, "but zinc deficiency may also result in smaller sex organs as a result of inadequate gonadotrophin. The late Professor Eric Underwood described gonadotrophin as a hormone which has a sexually stimulating effect on the sex glands of both males and females. Sufficient levels of this sex hormone are produced only in the presence of adequate zinc. All the other ingredients for the production of this hormone may be in your body, but if you lack zinc, your body won't produce gonadotrophin."

At this point I had my publisher's undivided attention, so I told him more about Professor Underwood's study in which he reported that spermatogenesis, the production of sperm, would not take place without a large amount of zinc in the system.

"From what you have told me," said my publisher, "it sounds possible that some impotence may be related to zinc deficiencies."

"That's probably true," I replied. "Not only is zinc involved in spermatogenesis, the development of primary and secondary sex organs and the sex drive, but it also is involved in every phase of the female reproductive process from estrus, which is the state of sexual excitability, to conceiving and actually giving birth."

"You might say that zinc is a very sexy mineral," the publisher joked.

I laughed and continued, "In a number of different studies, female test animals with dietary zinc deficiencies refused to mate and were infertile. When given zinc supplements, the females resumed normal mating habits. During pregnancies, if the female test animals were deprived of zinc, the pregnancies were aborted or resulted in death of the offspring at birth at an alarming rate of 50 percent. The late Dr. Lucile Hurley showed in her tests of laboratory animals that approximately 98 percent of the young from zinc-deficient mothers had birth defects. In another study, females who were zinc deficient were found to have extreme difficulty giving birth and experienced excessive bleeding during and after delivery.

"Apparently," I continued, "within genetic limits, there seems to be a direct relationship between the amount of zinc within the body and almost every aspect of both sexual functioning and sexual development."

"Do you recommend zinc supplements?" asked my friend.

"I concur with the National Research Council. Supplements are necessary for many people. However, some supplements, particularly those that have been properly chelated with amino acids, would probably be of benefit to almost anyone," I answered, "since the zinc content of most foods has shown a marked decline over the past twenty years, which has given rise to widespread deficiencies in the United States."

"Maybe you ought to include some of this information about zinc in the new book you're writing," said my publisher, bringing us back to the reason for my visit.

"I get the impression that you would rather read about my ideas than just hear me talk about them," I chuckled.

"Talk is cheap," he said, "but a manuscript would be worth some money."

NOTES

1. National Academy of Sciences, *Recommended Dietary Allowances* (Washington, DC: National Academy of Sciences, 1980), p. 144.
2. W. Pories, Address to the American Association for the Advancement of Science, Dallas, 1968.

ADDITIONAL READING

De Robertis, E., *et al.*, *Cell Biology* (Philadelphia: W.B. Saunders Co.), 1975.

Pories, W., *et al.*, eds., *Clinical Applications of Zinc Metabolism* (Springfield: Charles C Thomas), 1974.

Prasad, A., *Zinc in Human Nutrition* (Boca Raton: C.R.C. Press, Inc.), 1979.

National Academy of Sciences, *Recommended Dietary Allowances* (Washington, DC: National Academy of Science), 1980.

Allaway, W., *The Effect of Soils and Fertilizers on Human and Animal Nutrition* (Washington, DC: United States Dept. of Agriculture), 1975.

Hambridge, M. and Nichols, B., eds., *Zinc and Copper in Clinical Medicine* (New York: S.P. Medical & Scientific Books), 1978.

Prasad, A., ed., *Zinc Metabolism* (Springfield: Charles C Thomas), 1966.

Nancollas, G., ed., *Biological Mineralization and Demineralization* (Berlin: Springer-Verlag), 1982.

Pories, W., *Proc. American Assoc. Advancement Science*, Dallas, 1968.

Harvey, S., *Minerals: Right on Target* (Orem: Nature's Field), 1987.

Manspeaker, J., "Chelated amino acid minerals: Their role in bovine fertility," paper presented at the Pan American Congress of Veterinary Medicine and Zootechnique, 1986.

Underwood, E., *Trace Minerals in Human and Animal Nutrition* (New York: Academic Press), 196 – 242, 1977.

Ashmead, H., "Metabolic systems and their mineral activators," paper given at a Miller Seminar for physicians, Denver, 1968.

Brewer, G. and Prasad A., eds., *Zinc Metabolism: Current Aspects in Health and Disease* (New York: Alan R. Liss, Inc.), 1977.

22

Zinc to See

The other night my wife and I visited some friends. After a few minutes of conversation the husband invited me to accompany him to the den, where he wanted to show me a recently purchased piece of sculpture.

As I followed him to his den we passed a room where his three children were seated in front of a television watching a program. Our passing happened to coincide with a commercial, which caught my interest. My friend paused too and we both watched.

The sponsor of the television program was a vitamin manufacturer. The advertisement addressed the fact that nine out of ten children in the United States were not getting sufficient iron from their diets. Consequently, the product this company was promoting included iron in combination with vitamins.

"I can remember a few years ago when no one included iron with their vitamins," my friend observed. "Today, I see it being added as a supplement to breakfast cereals, breads, and many other foods. Now it appears that even the major vitamin manufacturers are including iron. That's certainly an improvement."

"Yes it is," I agreed, "but most of them haven't gone far enough."

"What do you mean?" he wanted to know.

"In some instances I believe that the iron is included simply for appearance sake and not to improve the person's nutrition. What many are doing reminds me of the least-cost diet some farmers developed for their animals."

215

"What is a least-cost diet?"

"Just what the name implies," I answered. "The idea is to feed the animals or birds the cheapest feeds available, including, in some instances, recycled manure. The animal is supposed to grow and develop at a minimum expense to the farmer. The problem is that unless the animal receives all the nutrients that it truly needs to grow at its maximum genetic potential, the farmer may lose out in the long run. You can't produce something from nothing."

"What does a least-cost diet have to do with the iron that is being supplemented?" my friend wanted to know.

"The same principle applies," I explained. "Frequently the manufacturer will select the least expensive mineral source for inclusion in his product. When he does this, he is giving little thought to just how much of the mineral is available to the body. In some instances I have seen minerals included in the foods or supplements that the body can't even absorb. In those cases, I think the manufacturer is simply window-dressing his product and trying to lull the consumer into a false sense of security. The product meets label claims because government standards require that minerals be found in a chemical analysis. Unfortunately, our stomachs and intestines can't read, so our bodies still remain deficient. The chemical presence of a mineral is no guarantee that it is biologically available, and currently there are no bioavailability standards."

"What is the answer?"

"Based on the research I've been involved in for more than half my life, the minerals must be properly chelated with amino acids prior to ingestion," I told him.

"Then, if we assumed that the iron in that children's vitamin product as properly chelated, everything else would be satisfactory," my friend concluded.

I smiled and said, "Unfortunately, that is far from true. In studies conducted by Hambidge and Walravens and published in the book *Trace Elements in Human Health and Disease*, it appears that zinc deficiencies are common in the United States and probably occur as frequently as iron deficiencies. Further, the zinc blood levels in American children appear to be 20 percent to 30 percent lower than levels in children of equivalent ages in Sweden, Germany, and New Zealand."

"Why is zinc so important?" my friend asked.

"For one thing, as you probably already know, zinc deficiency adversely affects growth and development in children," I answered. "Without zinc to activate certain enzymes, protein metabolism is impossible. For example, if there is a zinc deficiency in the body, the amino acid methionine cannot be turned into tissue protein, the amino acid cystine cannot be converted to skin protein, and collagen synthesis is impaired."

"Yes, but I am already an adult," my friend pointed out. "The biggest worry I have as far as growth and development are concerned is keeping my waistline trim."

I laughed. "You have got more problems than that. Your body is in a constant state of flux. Every day you build new skin cells, new tissues, new hair cells, etc., to replace those that have worn out and died or been destroyed. Inadequate zinc impairs the efficiency through which those metabolic changes can occur.

"But that's not all. Research has indicated that zinc deficiencies prevent vitamin A from being utilized by the body. This means that perhaps many of us who are taking vitamin supplements may be deficient in zinc, and therefore we are wasting the money we are spending on the vitamin A supplements."

My friend was immediately intrigued. "You mean zinc and vitamin A are synergistic?"

"Definitely," I answered. "This interrelationship was first suspected in 1956 when scientists published findings in the *Journal of Animal Science*. They noted that dietary deficiencies of zinc resulted in vitamin A deficiencies in the blood. It took almost twenty additional years for scientists to actually discover what the relationship was."

"What is it?"

"The problem is mobilization of vitamin A from the liver," I explained. "Supplements of vitamin A are stored in the liver as they are absorbed. However, getting the vitamin A from the liver to other parts of the body, such as the retina of the eyes, requires a special transport protein. Zinc is involved in the synthesis of that transport protein."

"So if there is a zinc deficiency, the transport protein is not manufactured and what vitamin A is absorbed cannot be mobilized and utilized," my friend concluded.

"That's right," I agreed.

"You mentioned moving vitamin A to the eyes," my friend continued. "Is that important?"

"Absolutely," I told him. "The retina of the eye contains one of the highest concentrations of zinc in the body. One of the reasons it is there is to transport the vitamin A to the eye.

"Do you remember when you were a kid you were told to eat lots of carrots for your eyes?" He nodded affirmatively.

"Carrots contain carotene, a precursor to vitamin A. A certain amount of vitamin A is needed to prevent night blindness. I remember reading about a recent German study involving seventy-five people with chronic liver disease. This liver disease caused a zinc deficiency in the liver, which presumably reduced the production of vitamin A transport protein. The study concluded that 45 percent of those people were potentially dangerous drivers because they had decreased twilight visual acuity and increased sensitivity to dazzle. Although this was directly due to the lack of vitamin A, it was probably actually caused by a zinc deficiency."

"I doubt if I have a zinc deficiency since I can certainly see the importance of getting adequate zinc," my friend said jokingly as he played on the words. Then becoming serious he asked, "What foods should I be eating?"

"It is not as simple as that," I answered. "Dr. Oberleas of the University of Kentucky and Dr. Harland of the US Food and Drug Administration have concluded that it is impossible to use the zinc content of foods as a measurement of the zinc status of the body. Part of the food we eat is neither digested nor absorbed and changes little as it travels through the intestines. This in turn affects the availability of nutrients such as zinc and may even contribute to their depletion. Both fiber and phytic acid are in this class and both reduce the amount of zinc absorbed. Other minerals such as calcium, lead, mercury, iron, copper, and cadmium also offset zinc absorption. The amount of protein in the diet directly influences the quantity of zinc absorbed."

"What's the protein for?" my friend wanted to know.

"There is not total agreement in the case of zinc; many believed that picolinic acid was needed for zinc absorption, but recent research has discredited picolinic acid. I believe most research has shown that before the zinc is absorbed it must be chelated with amino acids," I explained. "Presumably that dietary protein serves as a source for these amino acids."

"Then I don't need to worry about taking prechelated zinc," he concluded. "The body will do it for me."

"I would worry if I were you," I answered. 'The body will do some chelating, and some zinc may be absorbed. Generally, however, no more than 20 percent is ever absorbed. University research sponsored by Albion Laboratories has shown that when the zinc is properly chelated with amino acids, considerably more of it is absorbed through the intestines into the body."

My friend was going to say something else when his children reminded us that we were still standing by the television and that our conversation was interfering with their program. With that reminder we moved into his den to see his new sculpture.

ADDITIONAL READING

Ashmead, H.D., *et al.*, *Intestinal Absorption of Metal Ions and Chelates* (Springfield: Charles C. Thomas), 1985.

Prasad, A., ed., *Trace Elements in Human Health and Disease* (New York: Academic Press), V. 1, 1976.

Brewer, G. and Prasad, A., eds., *Zinc Metabolism: Current Aspects in Health and Disease* (New York: Alan R. Liss, Inc.), 1977.

Daniel, H., *et al.*, "Effectors of small intestinal zinc absorption-studies with an *in vitro* perfusion technique and on brush border membrane vesicles," poster presented at Bioavailability 88 Conference, Norwich, England, August 1988.

Schricker, B., *Studies of an endogenous zinc chelator of rat intestine* (University of Illinois Ph.D. Thesis) 1978.

Inglett, G., ed., *Nutritional Bioavailability of Zinc* (Washington, DC: American Chemical Society), 1983.

23

The Roles of Zinc and Other Minerals in Preventing Senility and Aging

Jean, a business associate, and I were sitting at a Paris sidewalk cafe when a woman bent over with age hobbled by. She was accompanied by a younger woman, presumably her daughter, who chided her mother in an obvious effort to hurry her along.

"It's tough to grow old," Jean said.

"Yes, I know what you mean," I groaned. "The older I get, the longer it takes me to overcome the effects of jet lag when I come to Europe." "No," Jean replied. "I was referring to that crippled old lady who just walked by. It's sad to see how age has removed much of her dignity."

"There's not much we can do about it, though," I said, still engrossed in my own discomfort. "From the moment of birth, we begin the road to old age. The maximum life span for humans is probably about 120 years, and the average is much less than that."

"It's as if we were genetically programmed to age," Jean commented.

"Yes, but I don't think a lot of the problems associated with aging are genetically programmed. I think they are a matter of environment."

"What do you mean?" he wanted to know.

"Take the old woman you observed," I explained. "I would guess that she is senile to a certain degree. Assuming this is true, I would speculate that you would also find certain metals at near toxic levels in her body."

221

"I know you well enough to recognize when you're trying to make a point," Jean observed. "What are you driving at this time?"

"In studies reported in 1977, researchers confirmed that aluminum can be a contributing factor in senility."

"How does that happen?" questioned my friend.

"I'm not certain of all the causal relationships," I confessed. "Right now I don't think anyone is. I do know that research at Albion Laboratories has shown that in the presence of aluminum, calcium will come out of solution rapidly and plate itself to various media. This may help explain how the aluminum contributes to senility."

"I suppose you're referring to the relationship between senility and atherosclerosis," commented my friend.

"Exactly," I responded. "In an article published in the 1974 issue of *Lancet*, Dr. V.C. Hachinski described the appearance of the brain of a senile person. He observed an atherosclerotic buildup of calcium in the arteries of the brain that could diminish the flow of blood and possibly cause ruptures or strokes."

"If this excessive intake of aluminum comes from the environment," Jean questioned, "why aren't we seeing senility at all age levels?"

"I think we are," I answered. "It simply becomes more acute and more prevalent in older people as a result of buildup over time. Although this is an unconfirmed theoretical concept, consider the following possibility: As a person becomes older, the increased accumulation of aluminum causes more calcium to be taken out of the blood and deposited on the arterial walls. When this occurs the calcium and zinc are thrown out of balance, because the increased deposition of calcium causes excessive amounts of zinc to leave the body. It's a vicious cycle which results in increased susceptibility to senility.

"Now, by supplementing the diet with extra biologically available zinc—that is, zinc amino acid chelates—a more natural balance between zinc and calcium is attained in the blood and tissues. The calcium can't be 'plaqued out' as easily as before because the zinc is there to prevent that from happening. The result is certainly less atherosclerosis and possibly less senility."

"Where does all of this accumulated aluminum come from?" Jean asked.

"You'd be surprised," I replied. "Aluminum is one of the most abundant minerals on the face of the earth. In an editorial that appeared in the May 1980 issue of *Bestways*, Barbara Bassett reported that aluminum is found as an anti-caking agent in table salt, an emulsifier in processed cheese, a bleaching agent in flour, and as a major ingredient in many antacids, not to mention aluminum foil, aluminum cans, and aluminum cookware. Each of these and other sources contribute minute amounts of aluminum to the diet, which, over time and age, can build up into a potentially toxic state contributing directly to senility."

"Is there anything a person can do to avoid the detrimental effects of aluminum?" inquired my friend. "It sounds as if none of us can help being exposed to it."

"As I alluded to earlier, there is some evidence that zinc may play a role in reducing the harmful effects of aluminum," I responded. "In research reported by Dr. Anthony Czerwenski in the April 1974 issue of the *Journal of Chemical Pharmacology and Therapeutics*, it was suggested that zinc may help in some cases of senility. The rationale for use of zinc is that blood plasma levels and cellular tissue levels tend to decrease with age, and zinc has enjoyed some success in reversing atherosclerosis. In the experiments of Czerwenski, brain damage senility was not reversed, but there was the suggestion that zinc supplements may help prevent senility from starting."

"Why is that?" my friend questioned.

"I don't have the total answer," I replied, "but turning back to research on the relationship of zinc to calcium, it was found that these two minerals must be kept in balance. If the body level of one is elevated, the other is depressed. As you know, in each of our body cells the major bearer of genetic information is DNA. It is located in the nucleus or central core of the cell. The transfer of genetic information and the genetic code for the DNA of that specific cell is copied onto molecules of RNA. The RNA then functions as the pattern used by the cell to synthesize the various proteins needed by the cell to duplicate itself. If the wrong mineral is present at any step during the genetic transfer, mistakes can be made. In fact, even an excess of essential minerals can cause the process to go haywire.

"Recently it has been discovered that in the RNA synthesis step of the bacterial cell *E. coli*, zinc is required along with either manganese, magnesium, or cobalt in order to activate a specific enzyme. Manganese is the most active and cobalt the least active of the three, but only magnesium allows the complete synthesis of the RNA. Conversely, a higher than optimum level of magnesium may cause an ambiguity in the protein synthesis.

"The result of these two conditions," I continued, "is an error in the transfer of genetic information and the incorporation of the wrong amino acids into cellular protein. Now the cell, being genetically different from its predecessor, begins to function differently and potentially accelerates aging and possibly even contributes to senility."

"In other words," Jean observed, "we need the correct balance of a number of minerals to insure proper functioning of the system and to avoid some of the problems we observed in the old woman."

"That's right," I agreed. "Now I just wish that someone would learn how to deal with jet lag."

ADDITIONAL READING

Hachinski, V., "Multi-infarct dementia. A cause of mental deterioration in the elderly," *Lancet*, 2:207, July 27, 1974.

Ashmead, D., ed., *Chelated Mineral Nutrition in Plants, Animals and Man* (Springfield: Charles C. Thomas), 1982.

Basset, B., Editorial, *Bestways*, May 1980.

Czerwenski, A., *J. of Chemical Pharmacology and Therapeutics*, April 1974.

Ashmead, H.D., *et al.*, eds., *Foliar Feeding of Plants with Amino Acid Chelates* (Park Ridge: Noyes Publications), 1986.
Ashmead, H., "Tissue Transportation of organic trace minerals," *J. Appl. Nutri.*, 22:42, Spring 1970.
Giese, A., *Cell Physiology* (Philadelphia: Saunders College), 1973.

24

A Philosophical Conclusion

A ll human nutrition is derived from six basic nutrients:
(1) protein, (2) carbohydrates, (3) fats, (4) water, (5) vitamins, and (6) minerals.[1] Because these nutrients are absolutely essential for energy, growth and maintenance of tissues, and regulation of body processes, government agencies and scientific bodies around the world have expended considerable effort to establish optimal amounts for each nutrient to maximize their functions.

The National Academy of Science in Washington, DC, in its publication *Recommended Dietary Allowances*, stated, "Recommended Dietary Allowances (RDA) are the levels of intake of essential nutrients considered in the judgment of the Committee on Dietary Allowances of the Food and Nutrition Board on the basis of available scientific knowledge, to be adequate to meet the known nutritional needs of practically all healthy persons . . . RDA should not be confused with requirements for a specific individual."[2] RDA are established for healthy populations.[2]

Recognizing individual differences and needs, Simko, *et al.* listed five groups of conditions that could affect the RDA that an individual is able to obtain: (1) inadequate nutrient intake,

In August 1988, I was invited to participate at an international conference entitled Bioavailability 88. Held in Norwich, England, the conference dealt with nutrient bioavailability. I made two presentations at that conference. This is one of those presentations, "The Need for New Nutrient Reference Standards."

(2) inadequate nutrient absorption, (3) defective nutrient utilization, (4) increased nutrient excretion, and (5) increased nutrient requirements to meet specific conditions.[3]

As comprehensive as their list is, it fails to recognize a major factor that affects individual nutritional status and cuts across and frequently invalidates the RDA. That factor is the dynamic change in nutrient bioavailability based on the chemical form, the food source and its preparation, and the presence or absence of other nutrients in the same meal. For example, the USRDA assumes that if a food contains 18 mg of iron in the form of a salt, the RDA for iron for adult women has been met, even though the iron salt may be insoluble and thus unavailable. As a nutrient it may be present but the body may not be able to absorb it. Similarly, if inorganic ions are initially present but become bound to other food constituents such as phosphates or phytic acid, they may become insoluble and worthless to nutrition. Most studies do not recognize the changes in nutrient bioavailability as a concern in establishing dietary recommendations; nevertheless, it should receive consideration. To illustrate, it is estimated that up to 70 percent of certain groups of Americans are able to obtain only two-thirds of the RDA for vitamins from their food.[4,5] Freezing and heating of foods destroys the vitamin content, and causes a loss of amino acids.[6,7,8,9] The length of storage after processing also affects nutritive values.[10]

Gross chemical analyses of the energy portion of the diet (carbohydrates and fats) would suggest little change in consumption over the past two decades. And yet there has been approximately a 54 percent reduction in the intake of complex carbohydrates and a corresponding increase of about 50 percent of ingestion of simple sugars.[11] During this same period there has been a 37 percent increase in the ratio of unsaturated to polyunsaturated fatty acids.[11] Thus while food energy levels have not changed dramatically, their nutritive value has. There is an excess of empty calories as seen in decreases of essential fatty acids in the diet with corresponding increases in saturated fats, cholesterol, and refined sugars.[12]

Katz, *et al.*, have reported a relative and/or absolute decline in the mineral values of the foods we eat.[12] This reflects among other things a 13 percent decrease in iron and a 3 percent decrease in calcium.[13] Copper intake is declining in Western countries as a result of prepackaging foods[25] and is leading to observations of significantly lower dietary intakes of copper than recommended by the World Health Organization or RDA.[26] The average American diet contains between 11 mg and 13 mg of zinc, which is below the RDA of 15 mg. Processing further depletes the zinc from food.[27] Although dietary iron has increased from 15 to 17.6 mg per day, a nationwide food consumption survey revealed that an adequate diet will normally provide only 6 mg of iron.[29] Further, there is no general agreement on intestinal absorption of essential minerals: Estimates of calcium absorption range from 10 percent to 50 percent of the dose. Zinc uptake can fluctuate between approximately 5 percent and 30 percent. Magnesium absorption ranges between 25 percent and 75 percent of the administered dose. The values for manganese absorption have been reported to be between 3 percent and 97 percent. Normal iron absorption ranges between 2 percent and 20 percent.[14]

Why is there no general agreement? Kies answered, "If nutrients found in food were digested, absorbed, and made available to the human at the 100 percent level, the science and practice of nutrition would be simplified. That nutrients vary in their bioavailability has been well established. The chemical nature of the specific form of the nutrient involved, the chemical and physical characteristics of the foods in which nutrients are contained, other constituents of the diet, the nature of the digestive and absorptive processes for the specific nutrients, and the physiological condition of the person consuming the food all may affect bioavailability."[30]

Using iron as the example, Sandstead has reported, "Absorption of Fe from foods of plant origin is generally poor, while absorption from meat is much better. Certain fractions of dietary fiber, phytate, and other substances derived from plants impair Fe absorption, while heme Fe from meat is highly bioavailable. Gastric acid facilitates the dissociation of Fe from plant-binding ligands and its reduction to the ferrous state. Ascorbic acid also facilitates these processes. Meat improves Fe absorption through an ill-defined mechanism. The Fe status of individuals determines how avidly they absorb Fe. Thus, dietary composition, its heme and nonheme Fe content, the physiologic integrity of the intestinal tract, and the level of Fe nutriture of individuals all modulate Fe absorption and retention and determine the amount of Fe necessary in diets to satisfy homeostatic requirements."[15]

To alleviate many of these problems, an increasing number of nutritionists have turned to chelated minerals. Their philosophy is based on the belief that chelation of a mineral is a natural step in the absorption and use of the mineral by the body. When non-amino acid chelated minerals, such as sulfates or gluconates, arrive in the intestine they must be ionized and chelated with available dietary amino acids prior to absorption.[16] While this description of absorption is oversimplified and has minor flaws,[17] the theory continues that minerals which are prechelated with amino acids prior to ingestion sidestep the digestive problems with other forms of minerals and increase their uptake.[16] Because of the reputation for better absorption, Rosenberg and Feldzamen conclude, "So look for the words chelated minerals when you buy a mineral supplement."[18]

The words chelated minerals do not guarantee either mineral absorption or metabolism.[19] Using different protein sources for the amino acid ligands caused variations in chelate absorption of 79 percent in copper, 68 percent in magnesium, 273 percent in iron, and 52 percent for zinc.[20] Even using the same amino acid ligands while altering the chelation procedure changed the absorption levels of the metals involved.[21,22] In other tests, the use of non-amino acid chelating ligands, such as citric acid and gluconic acid, did not result in significantly elevated body mineral levels, even though they form true chelates.[23]

As a result of these data, those of us from Albion Laboratories, Inc., believe new standards of analysis for the nutritive bioavailability value of foods and supplements should be established. The current tables and charts are generally inaccurate. As Harris observed, "Food tables tend to give values that are too high."[24] Further, the new standards should not be based on the total quantity of the nutrient in the food or supplement because its presence does not guarantee either availability or biological utilization.

Conversely, values ought to be based on biological utilization rather than chemical quantity. The naturally occurring iron that is tightly bound to phytic acid in bread[28] does the body no more good than does an empty calorie. Instead of conducting chemical analyses to ascertain sufficiency of nutrient levels we should be concentrating on standardized metabolic studies that describe the biological utilization of each nutrient in all of its various forms—chemical and naturally occurring in foods. Admittedly this is a formidable task, but we must accept the challenge if we hope to understand and practice effective nutrition.

REFERENCES

1. Guthrie, Helen A., *Introductory Nutrition*. (St. Louis: Times Mirror/ Mosby) 11, 1986.
2. Munro, H., *et al.*, *Recommended Dietary Allowances*. (Washington, DC: National Academy of Sciences) 1, 1980.
3. Simko, M., C. Cowell, J. Gilbride, *Nutrition Assessment* (Rockville: Aspen Systems Corp.) 6, 1984.
4. Goodhart, R.S., "How well nourished are Americans?" *National Vitamin Foundation Report for 1960*, New York, July 1961.
5. Goodhart, R., "How well nourished are Americans? II" *National Vitamin Foundation Report for 1961 – 1963*. New York.
6. Pearson, A., R. West, and R. Luecke. "The vitamin and amino acid content of drip obtained upon defrosting frozen pork," *Food Res.* 24:515, 1959.
7. Betterworth, M., and C. Fox, "The effects of heat treatment on the nutritive value of coconut meal, and the prediction of nutritive value by chemical methods," *Brit. J. Nutr.*, 17:445, 1963.
8. Clarke, J., and B. Kennedy, "Availability of lysine in whole wheat bread and selected breakfast cereals," *J. Food Sci.*, 27:609, 1962.
9. Gates, J., and B. Kennedy, "Protein quality of bread and bread ingredients," *J. Am. Diet Assoc.*, 44:374, 1964.

10. Longenecker, J., and H. Sarett, "Nutritional quality of survival biscuits and crackers," *Am. J. Clin. Nutr.*, 13:291, 1963.
11. Antar, M., M. Ohlson, and R. Hodges, "Changes in retail market food supplies in the United States in the last seventy years in relation to the incidence of coronary heart disease with special reference to dietary carbohydrate and essential fatty acids," *Am. J. Clin. Nutr.*, 14:169, 1964.
12. Katz, L., J. Stamler, and R. Pick, *Nutrition and Antherosclerosis.* (Philadelphia: Lea & Febiger) 16 – 20, 1958.
13. Hubbard, A., "The American diet paradox," *Modern Med. Topics*, 23:12, December 1962.
14. Ashmead, H.D., D. Graff, and H. Ashmead, *Intestinal Absorption of Metal Ions and Chelates* (Springfield: Charles C Thomas) 24 – 25, 1985.
15. Sandstead, H., "Are estimates of trace element requirements meeting the needs of the user?" in Mills, C., I. Bremner, and J. Chesters, eds., *Trace Elements in Man and Animals* (Farnham: Commonwealth Agricultural Bureau) 875, 1985.
16. Hoffer, A. and M. Walker, *Orthomolecular Nutrition* (New Canaan: Keats Publishing Inc.) 151, 1978.
17. Ashmead, H.D., *op cit.*, 103.
18. Rosenberg, H. and A. Feldzamen, *The Book of Vitamin Therapy* (New York: Perigee Books) 172, 1974.
19. Ashmead, H., D. Ashmead, and N. Jensen, "Chelation does not guarantee mineral metabolism," *J. Applied Nutr.*, 26:5, Summer 1974.
20. Graff, D., H. Ashmead, and C. Hartley, "Absorption of minerals compared with chelates made from various protein sources into rat jejunal slices *in vitro*," paper presented at Utah Academy of Arts, Letters and Sciences, Salt Lake City, April 1970.
21. Jensen, N., "Biological Assimilation of Metals," U.S. Patent # 4,167,564, September 23, 1974.
22. Beck, B., "Comparison of true chelated amino acid chelates," unpublished, September 1976.
23. Soffer, A., *Chelation Therapy* (Springfield: Charles C Thomas) 6 and 102, 1964.
24. Harris, R., "Food composition and availability of nutrients in foods," *Am. J. Clin. Nutr.*, 11:400, 1962.
25. Danks, D., "Copper deficiency in humans," in Evered, D., and G. Lawrenson, eds., *Biological Roles of Copper* (Amsterdam: Excerpta Medica) 209, 1980.
26. Delves, H., "Dietary sources of copper," in Evered, D., and G. Lawrenson, eds., *Biological Roles of Copper* (Amsterdam: Excerpta Medica) 5, 1980.
27. Prasad, A., "Experimental zinc deficiency in humans," in Inglett, G., ed., *Nutritional Bioavailability of Zinc* (Washington, DC: American Chemical Society) 1, 1983.
28. Morris, E. and R. Ellis, "Phytate, wheat bran and bioavailability of dietary iron," in Kies, C., ed., *Nutritional Bioavailability of Iron* (Washington, DC: American Chemical Society) 121, 1982.

29. Guthrie, H., *op cit.*, 254 – 256.
30. Kies, C., *Nutritional Bioavailability of Iron* (Washington, DC: American Chemical Society) IX, 1982.

Name Index

Subject Index